VOLUME 2

Miss Brenda's

BEDTIME STORIES

This book is lovingly presented to

_____

By: _____

On this special occasion

_____

Date: _____

VOLUME 2

Miss Brenda's
BEDTIME STORIES

BRENDA WALSH

Based on
True Character-Building Stories
for the Whole Family!

3ABN BOOKS

Three Angels Broadcasting Network
P.O. Box 220, West Frankfort, Illinois
www.3ABN.org

Pacific Press® Publishing Association
Nampa, Idaho
Oshawa, Ontario, Canada
www.pacificpress.com

Design/Layout: Chrystique Neibauer "CQ" I cqgraphicdesign.com
Cover Photography: David B. Sherwin
Project Coordinator: Mellisa Hoffman I finaleditservices.com

The author assumes full responsibility for the accuracy of all facts and quotations as cited in this book.

Additional copies of this book are available from two locations:

Adventist Book Centers®: Call toll-free 1-800-765-6955 or visit http://www.adventistbookcenter.com.

3ABN: Call (618) 627-4651 or visit http://www.store.3abn.org.

3ABN Books is dedicated to bringing you the best in published materials consistent with the mission of Three Angels Broadcasting Network. Our goal is to uplift Jesus Christ through books, audio, and video materials by our family of 3ABN presenters. Our in-depth Bible study guides, devotionals, biographies, and lifestyle materials promote whole person health and the mending of broken people. For more information, call 618-627-4651 or visit 3ABN's Web site: www.3ABN.org.

Scripture quotations marked NIV are from the HOLY BIBLE, NEW INTERNATIONAL VERSION®. Copyright © 1973, 1978, 1984 by International Bible Society. Used by permission of Zondervan Publishing House. All rights reserved.

Scriptures quoted from NKJV are from The New King James Version, copyright © 1979, 1980, 1982, Thomas Nelson, Inc., Publishers.

Scripture quotations marked NLT are taken from the Holy Bible, New Living Translation, copyright © 1996, 2004, 2007. Used by permission by Tyndale House Publishers, Inc., Wheaton, Illinois 60189. All rights reserved.

Scripture quotations marked KJV are from the King James Version of the Bible.

Library of Congress Cataloging-in-Publication Data:

Walsh, Brenda, 1953-
Miss Brenda's bedtime stories : true character building stories for the whole family! / Brenda Walsh.
        p. cm.
ISBN 13: 978-0-8163-2491-0 (hard cover)
ISBN 10: 0-8163-2491-3 (hard cover)
1. Christian children—Religious life—Anecdotes. 2. Families—Religious life—Anecdotes.
I. Title. II. Title: Bedtime stories.
BV4571.3.W35 2011
249—dc22
                                                                                        2011007590

11 12 13 14 15 • 5 4 3 2 1

Pastor James and Bernice Micheff

It is with deep love and gratitude that I dedicate volume two of *Miss Brenda's Bedtime Stories* to my precious parents, James and Bernice Micheff, who have committed their lives to serving Jesus. I can shut my eyes and still hear Dad's cheery voice calling my brothers and sisters and me to worship.

I can't remember a day that didn't start and end with family worship. We would all snuggle up on the sofa together, and Mom would read to us. Mom and Dad always chose books that would inspire us to be more like Jesus. We were not allowed to read just anything. Our books were approved by our parents first! They felt that what their children read was critically important and if it wasn't going to bring us closer to Jesus, it was not allowed in our home!

If it were not for my parents' constant effort to keep me in touch with God through His Word and other character-building stories, *Miss Brenda's Bedtime Stories* would not have been written.

Mom and Dad, I want to dedicate this book first to Jesus, my Lord and Savior, and then to both of you. It is my heartfelt prayer that as children around the world read these inspiring stories, their lives will be transformed. Thank you for your commitment to ever inspire your children to love Jesus.

I love you with all my heart and thank God for the blessings of having Christian parents. I also thank you for making Jesus *first* in our home, and because of you, my greatest passion in life is to share God's love with others.

It is my deepest desire that the prayer you have prayed my entire life be fulfilled, when *"someday soon we will all be gathered together in heaven as a family . . . without one lost!"* I love you, Mom and Dad!

ACKNOWLEDGMENTS

With Special Thanks

Dr. Kay Kuzma

I want to thank Dr. Kay Kuzma for all her hours and hours spent editing *Miss Brenda's Bedtime Stories*. She is one of the most generous, kind, and talented people I know and these stories would not have been the same without her! I admire and respect her professionalism, creative writing skills, and her loving service for others. Her love for our Lord and Savior shines through in all she does. She has blessed my life in so many ways and I thank God for the gift of her friendship.

Brenda Walsh

Author Appreciation

I want to personally thank each of these best-selling authors for their generous contribution of stories. It is truly an honor and privilege to include them in *Miss Brenda's Bedtime Stories*. Each author was personally selected to be a part of this five book series because of their creative and professional writing style, incredible talent, and love for Jesus! To each of them, I extend my sincere and heartfelt thanks!

Karen Collum

Kay Kuzma

Seth Pierce

Kay D. Rizzo

Glen Robinson

Gwen Simmons

Kimberley Tagert-Paul

Jerry D. Thomas

Joy Wendt

Perri Wiggins

ACKNOWLEDGMENTS

With Heartfelt Thanks To . . .

MY STORY AND PHOTO TEAM: *Bahamas Academy* for posing for photographs. *Battle Creek Academy* for opening your doors for the cover photo shoot. *Ted and Bonnie Bloomfield* for the many hours spent developing the Excel spreadsheet. *Mark and Conna Bond and family* for posing and taking photos, but most of all for your friendship and all the years you have supported my ministry in so many various capacities. *Tom, Gwen, and Kameron Hanna* for posing for photographs, friendship, and always being there for me! *Mellisa Hoffman* for your project coordination, organizational skills, being the "spelling champ," tenacity to *getting the job done*, and your loyalty and friendship! *Hannah and Lance Hoffman* for your patience during all the long hours your mom spent working on the book project. *Cori Holingsead* for taking photos at a moment's notice and being such an awesome friend! *Dr. Buddy and Tina Houghtaling* for organizing and planning the cover photo shoot, and all the years you dedicated your life to *Kids' Time*! *Chrystique Neibauer* for the incredible layout and graphic design of the entire project, for extra long hours, patience, and being a friend I can count on! *Dick and Lucy Neuharth* for photos and your treasured friendship! *Dave Sherwin* for volunteering your time to photograph each cover. *Ina Stanaland* for writing endless emails and reading and categorizing all the stories. *Gene, Melisa, and Holly Thompson* for love, support, friendship, and taking and posing in photos. I appreciate and love you all so very much.

MY MINISTRY SUPPORT TEAM: *Carole Derry-Bretsch* for emailing your numerous friends to find the perfect photos and, most of all, for being my lifelong friend! *Peg O'Brien Bernhard* for always being there for me, listening, believing in me, and for your love and friendship! *Kari Avery-Duffy* for hours spent researching stories, answering letters, and your dedication to the *Kids' Time* Ministries. *Marie Macri* for being a precious friend—always there for me. I love you dearly! *Rita Showers* for a lifetime of memories, friendship, and the best neighbor a girl could have! *Nancy Sterling* for mentoring me, looking out for my best interests, and for your loving friendship!

MY FAMILY: My precious husband, *Tim Walsh*, for never complaining about the time I spent working on this project, for your constant support, help, and patience, but most of all, for your unconditional love you give me every day! *Rebecca Lynn and Linda Kay* for your love and support and allowing me to share your stories. My parents, *James and Bernice Micheff,* for your prayers, letting my team take over your house, for endless hours finding photos, and for all those great meals! To my *sisters, brothers, grandsons, aunts, uncles, nieces, and nephews* for your patience and loving understanding concerning the many hours I spent working on this project, even though you would have preferred I was spending time with you! I am so very grateful for my precious family and love you with all my heart!

Those who shared their stories with me:

Sherry Christensen	Judy & Joshua Lance	Theresa Saxon
Michael & Jason Coffin	Mary Le Grice	Charles Mason von Henner, MD
Rebecca Coffin	Tim & Tara Pierce	Karen Yingst
Doloris Kiney	Andy Rissing	Debbie West

ABOUT "MISS BRENDA"

3ABN Kids' Time

Miss Brenda & Maxwell

Brenda Walsh is a vivacious, loving, and generous Christian with a heart for ministry and a burning desire to share the love and joy of Jesus. When she started praying, "Lord, use me in a special way," God did! And the resulting amazing miracle stories have been an inspiration to thousands across the world who have heard her dynamic presentations or read her attention-grabbing books. Her message is one of encouragement and hope to those who want to be used by God. Hearing Brenda is truly a life-changing experience whether it's at a women's ministries retreat, a prayer conference, a church-based weekend event, or a family or children's ministries seminar.

Brenda is best known as "Miss Brenda," the producer and host of **Kids' Time**, a popular daily children's program on Three Angels Broadcasting Network (3ABN). She is also a frequent guest on the 3ABN *Today* program, cooking and singing with her sisters, Linda and Cinda. Together they have authored vegan vegetarian cookbooks and recorded several gospel CDs. Brenda also has her own solo CD, **My Wonderful Lord**.

Brenda is the author of **Battered to Blessed**, her life story of being a victim of domestic violence, and **Passionate Prayer**, which features her own personal stories of answered prayer. She has also co-authored several books with her friend, Kay Kuzma. This is her second of five volumes of **Miss Brenda's Bedtime Stories**.

In addition to ministering to others, Brenda is a registered nurse, interior decorator, and floral designer. Brenda is married to Tim Walsh, has two grown daughters, Becky and Linda Kay, and two grandsons, Michael James and Jason Patrick.

www.kidstime4jesus.org

LESSON INDEX

TABLE OF CONTENTS

INTRODUCTION

Stories have power to touch us and change us. They can help us understand what another person is feeling and help us see things from a new perspective. They can help us understand "Why?" and see the reasoning behind "Be careful!" They can help us learn lessons without having to suffer from making mistakes! That's why Jesus taught by telling stories. He knew that stories help us understand.

This book is full of stories told for the same reasons. So much effort, love, and prayer have gone into collecting and preparing *Miss Brenda's Bedtime Stories*! Based on true stories contributed from people around the world, each one has been written especially for Miss Brenda by beloved and best-selling authors (and some written by Miss Brenda herself!). They are sure to be loved by children and treasured by parents and grandparents and all who read them.

Brenda has shared these stories to help kids everywhere develop strong characters, understand important lessons, and most important, learn to be a good friend of Jesus. These pages are full of stories that are heart-touching, soul-searching, fun-filled, adventurous, and meant to be shared!

May these stories bring laughter to the eyes, wisdom to the mind, and understanding to the heart of everyone who hears them. And may there be a double blessing of peace and joy to each grown-up who takes a few precious moments to share them with a child.

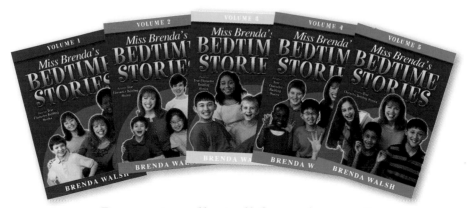

Be sure to collect all five volumes of
Miss Brenda's Bedtime Stories!

Polly's Pride

Polly balanced the silver flute in her hands. The cool metal against her fingers soothed the caterpillars of nerves that threatened to burst into full-blown butterflies in her stomach at any moment. Through the closed door she could hear the string quartet performing, the violins soaring over the deep tones of the cello.

She had peeked into the auditorium a little earlier and had felt a bubble of excitement well up when she saw just how many people had come to listen. The middle school concert was always popular, but this year there seemed to be an even bigger crowd.

I do hope all my friends are sitting up front where they can see me. They'll be so surprised at how good I can play. Oh, and there's Mom and Dad in the second row! They're going to be so proud of me! she thought as she brought the flute to her lips and let her fingers dance through a series of scales. Up and down, down and up, higher and higher, until she ran out of breath.

Polly played first flute in the concert band. As a sixth grader, she was the youngest person ever to be given the honor of first flute. She loved the way it felt to make music with other people, to take those little black circles and lines on a page and give them life. But more than that she loved the way it felt to be right up in front of the band for all the world to see.

Rearranging the pages on the music stand, Polly studied the piece once more. She was playing a difficult solo, the last item of the night. It was also the most coveted place in the program. When her teacher, Mr. Andrews, had first shown her the music she thought it was too hard. But he convinced her she could do it. She just needed to practice. And that's exactly what she did!

She practiced when she got up in the morning, she practiced during her lunch break at school, and she practiced before she went to bed at night. She practiced until she knew the music inside-out, upside-down, and backwards. Now she could play it from memory with her eyes closed.

The morning of the concert, Polly woke up suddenly with what she thought was a brilliant idea. *What if I went on stage without any music? Imagine how impressed everyone would be. Why, they'd all be talking about how talented I am. I might even get a standing ovation!*

All day long, Polly felt a nagging feeling in the pit of her stomach that just wouldn't go away. There was a still, small voice that kept telling her it was a bad idea, but she refused to listen.

That evening, she felt strangely nervous. *I don't know why I'm so nervous when I know my music so well. I don't need to fret like this. Maybe I'm just excited. Yes, that's it, just excited.*

"Polly, you're up," said Angela, who was working backstage.

With a deep breath, Polly stepped out of the rehearsal room balancing

her flute in her hands and walked with her head held high down the corridor.

"You forgot your music!" Angela called after her.

"I don't need it," said Polly, without even bothering to look back.

"Are you sure? What if you forget the notes?" Angela asked.

"Oh, that would never happen. I know this backwards and forwards, but thanks anyway," Polly confidently responded.

Polly waited in the wings for her name to be called, a small smile on her lips. Beyond the bright stage lights she could see the silhouettes of the audience. All those people were about to be dazzled by her brilliance.

The smile on her face beamed even brighter when she heard the announcer say, ". . . And for the final performance of the night, I'd like to welcome to the stage one of our finest young musicians here at Valley Middle School, Miss Polly Watson."

As the applause thundered around her, Polly stepped onto the wooden floor and strode across the stage to the perfect circle of light that shone just for her. She moved the empty music stand to one side so people would get a better view of her and then stood still, waiting for the clapping to stop. When silence finally filled the theater, Polly breathed deeply, lifted the flute to her lips, pulled her shoulders back, pursed her lips tight, and then the unimaginable happened . . . her mind went completely blank! She couldn't remember the first note! Even though she was blinded by the spotlight, she knew everyone was looking at her, waiting for her to begin. She could feel the anticipation, the expectation, and her mouth went dry.

Polly swallowed, ran her tongue over her lips, and tried not to panic. She closed her eyes and pictured the sheet music that was sitting on the music stand in the rehearsal room but the notes blurred into a swirl of nothingness. She was aware of the seconds ticking past, each one feeling like an hour. *I can't just stand up here and do nothing.*

MBBS2—2

Why can't I remember the notes? What's the matter with me? I need to play something . . . anything! Everyone's going to be laughing at me!

Polly blew feebly across the flute and sent a weak and whimpering note—a wrong note—across the audience. She tried another note. And another. Someone on the stage began to giggle. She could hear a snicker spreading through the audience. A crimson flush emerged from her chest and began to spread up her neck and onto her face, burning under the harsh light. She glanced to her right and saw Mr. Andrews backstage, his face wrinkled with worry. He motioned for her to try again, but it was no use. Polly couldn't remember a single note.

With the flute hanging from her left hand and tears streaming down her face, she ran off the stage, down the stairs, and into the rehearsal room, slamming the door behind her. The silence that followed her was louder than the marching band at a football game.

Polly slumped in a chair and sobbed for a long time, her head buried deep in her hands. Then she felt an arm around her shoulder. "Hey sweetie," said Mom tenderly.

Polly looked up through her tears, saw the love in her mom's eyes, and cried even harder. "I blew it," she sobbed. "I totally blew it."

"Honey, what happened? You knew that piece inside and out,"

said Mom. "Where was your sheet music?"

Polly blushed again and couldn't meet her mom's gaze as she tried to control her tears. Her voice was a mere whisper and the words tasted bitter in her mouth. "I left it behind on purpose because I wanted to impress everyone. I was going to be the star of the show. Instead, everyone's laughing at me." The sobs began again.

Mom tried to make her feel better

as she held Polly close and wiped away her tears. "Mom," Polly whispered, "it was my own fault. I was trying to show everyone how great I was."

Her mom gave her a gentle squeeze. "We all make mistakes, sweetie, but a wise person learns from them." Sweeping a loose strand of hair away from Polly's face, Mom continued, "Sounds to me like you let pride get in the way of common sense tonight."

Polly nodded.

"You know, the Bible says it best," said Mom. " 'When pride comes, then comes disgrace, but with humility comes wisdom' (Proverbs 11:2). I think you've learned a really important lesson tonight, Polly, and I'm sorry it's been such a painful one for you."

On the way home, Polly hugged her flute case to her chest and thought long and hard about what had happened that night. *Mom is right,* she thought. *I embarrassed myself in front of my family and all my friends. How will I ever face them tomorrow? I never want to make that mistake again.*

Polly closed her eyes and began to pray. *Dear Jesus, please forgive me for being so filled with pride. From now on, help me to listen to Your still, small voice and help me to use my talents for Your glory and not mine. I love You, Jesus. Amen.* ■

> *Pride goes before destruction, and a haughty spirit before a fall.*
> —Proverbs 16:18, NKJV

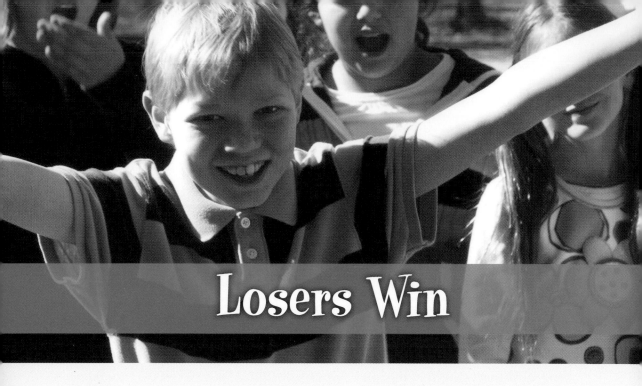

Losers Win

Jonathan loved all kinds of sports, but his favorite was dodge ball—and that was the game his class was scheduled to play during P.E. *One more hour and then it will be time for dodge ball,* he thought. When the bell rang, signaling the switch of classes, Jonathan hurried outside for gym class. He not only loved playing dodge ball, but he was also very good at it. In fact, the coach had even called him the *dodge ball king.*

There was one thing, however, that Jonathan didn't like about dodge ball, and that was how they selected the teams. The coach would call out the names of two kids to be team captains, and then they would select their teams by choosing the best players first. Jonathan was always among the first picked, but he could see how disappointed the weaker players were when they were always chosen last.

This was especially painful for Tyler and Crystal. You can't be good at everything, and they weren't the best in sports. But that didn't mean

they shouldn't be given a chance. Yet, when it came to dodge ball, Tyler and Crystal were always the last chosen. Jonathan could tell by the looks of disappointment on their faces that they were hurt by this.

Jonathan was really frustrated when, day after day, the same thing happened. The kids who were good at dodge ball enjoyed P.E. The kids who weren't, ended up feeling rejected and worthless.

It's not fair, thought Jonathan. *Why doesn't the coach just choose the teams by pulling names out of a hat or something? Even numbering off and letting all the number ones be one team, and the number twos be on another team would be a better way of choosing teams than good players first and poor players last.*

But day after day, the routine was the same. And day after day, Jonathan noticed the disappointment on Crystal's face each time she was overlooked. He would hold his breath as he watched Tyler waving his hand, wanting to get the captain's attention, and then limply withdrawing it when he was passed over. *Why doesn't anyone notice how rejected they feel?* If anyone did notice, they didn't seem to care. All they wanted to do was win.

It wasn't as if Jonathan didn't want to win. He enjoyed winning as much as the next person. But the great feeling of victory just didn't seem worth the bad feelings of what was happening to his friends.

Jonathan noticed something else. At the beginning of dodge ball season almost all the kids were excited about the game and wanted to participate. Now he could see that those who were chosen last had lost their desire to play. One time he overheard Crystal say, "Why try? The sooner I get put out, the sooner I can go and sit on the sidelines." Even Tyler had finally admitted, "I guess nobody really expects me to be able to get any better. So why try?"

Then one day everything changed. It was the day that the coach said, "Jonathan, you can be one of the captains today."

"OK," Jonathan said, as he walked up and stood beside the coach. *This is my chance! This is the day to make things different for Tyler and Crystal and the others who are chosen last.* Excitement built in Jonathan's chest as he looked the kids over, sizing up his team. *This is gonna be great!* Knowing that everyone would be expecting him to choose Brandon or another one of the good players first, he waited for silence before calling out the name of his first-choice player.

"Tyler," he called out in a loud, clear voice.

Tyler! A look of surprise passed over the faces of the star dodge ball players. Even the coach looked surprised. But no one was more shocked than Tyler himself who was in his usual spot waiting for the torture of the team selection to be over.

"D-d-did you call my name?" stuttered Tyler.

"Yeah," said Jonathan as though it happened every day. "Come on!"

In a state of shock, Tyler found himself jogging to the front to form the team line beside his captain. He couldn't believe that he had actually been chosen over Brandon and the other star players. *Wow, maybe I can do this,* he thought as his confidence built. *Maybe I can really make some good plays.*

The other captain chose Brandon. Then it was Jonathan's turn again.

"Crystal," Jonathan said in a loud voice. Once again everyone was surprised. *Jonathan must want to lose,* they all thought, but they didn't say anything.

As the selection continued, Jonathan kept choosing the poorest players first. Judging from past games, it was obvious to all that Jonathan's team was doomed to failure. There was no way his team could even come close to winning with all the lousy players. But interesting things can happen when people are given a fair chance and some encouragement.

Jonathan felt more excitement than ever before as he gathered his shocked, but delighted, team for a short pep talk.

"We can do it!" he said. "Let's go and show them that we're better than they think!" Team spirit built quickly, and as the game began, a strange thing happened. The opposite team, which was made up of many strong players, was not getting Jonathan's team out quite as quickly as they expected! The kids who they thought were weak players were now stepping up and giving the game all they had. Surprising even themselves, they were staying in longer and actually feeling a part of the team! Tyler felt confident as his captain cheered him on, and Crystal actually tried her best to stay in the game. They didn't want to sit on the sidelines. They wanted to play! And play they did!

So, who won the game? Well, it all depends on how you look at winning. By the rules of the game of dodge ball, Brandon's team won . . . barely. But judging by who felt the most like winners, it was clear that Jonathan's team came out ahead. Tyler, Crystal, and the others felt they were winners because someone believed in them and had given them a chance.

Jonathan would say he was a winner because he had experienced

the joy of choosing kids first who thought they were losers and helping them feel like winners.

Everyone loves to win, but putting others first and making them feel good about themselves is always the best way to do it. ∎

Let nothing be done through selfish ambition or conceit, but in lowliness of mind let each esteem others better than himself.
—Philippians 2:3 NKJV

Bringing Up Bosley

D ebbie loved animals. She always had lots of pets. She especially enjoyed raising them. So no one in the family was surprised when Debbie came home with another pet—especially a baby one.

One day, Debbie heard a terrible ruckus coming from the crows that lived in the huge eucalyptus trees in her yard. She rushed over to see what was happening. There on the ground under the tree was a fuzzy, little bird that a crow had dropped. It didn't look like a crow. And the way the crows were dive-bombing it, Debbie was afraid they were going to devour the poor little thing!

Quickly, she shooed the crows away, scooped up the tiny, white bird, and carried it into the house. And that's how Bosley became a part of the family.

"What kind of a bird is it?" Debbie asked her mom.

"I have no idea," she responded. "Maybe it's an owl."

Since Debbie didn't know what

kind of a bird it was, she had no idea what to feed it. "Why don't you call the vet?" suggested her mom.

When Debbie called, the vet said, "Feed the bird wet dog food because it has vitamins in it—and feed it every three hours. But don't be surprised if the bird doesn't live."

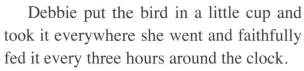

Debbie put the bird in a little cup and took it everywhere she went and faithfully fed it every three hours around the clock.

The whole family was shocked when Bosley lived through the first few days and began to grow more feathers. Debbie found an old rabbit cage, put a soft liner in it, and every day put wet dog food in the bowl for Bosley to eat.

Bosley grew and grew. Gray feathers grew on the bird's head and back, and brown and white feathers on its chest. The gray tail feathers grew longer and longer. Bosley looked like a little hawk, but since Debbie didn't know for sure what it was, she took Bosley to the owner of the pet store who was very knowledgeable about birds.

"It's a female sparrow hawk," she said.

"A female? Are you sure?" Debbie asked.

The store owner laughed and said, "Yes, I'm quite sure. But that doesn't mean you have to change her name. You can still call her Bosley. But you need to start feeding her some meat."

"What kind of meat?" Debbie asked, since she was a vegetarian and didn't have meat scraps in the house.

"Mice will do just fine—otherwise Bosley might get rickets in her legs and not be able to stand!" the lady replied.

"Mice? Yuck, that's disgusting! Where do I find mice meat?"

"Here at the pet store," she instructed. "If you want to keep this bird healthy, you're going to have to feed it two mice a week."

Gross, thought Debbie, *I'll never be able to do that.* But as the days went by, Debbie grew to love Bosley so much that she was willing to do anything to keep her alive, including feeding her mice! Debbie planned on keeping Bosley until she was old enough to feed herself, and then she would release her to the wild.

Bosley spent most of her time outside her cage sitting on a lamp or flying from place to place in the house. Bosley loved to sit by the window with the dogs and watch people and animals go by. Sometimes she sat on Debbie's head or her shoulder. But the funniest thing was to watch Bosley ride on the back of Tiffy, Debbie's teacup poodle.

It wasn't long before Bosley learned some sparrow hawk language. When she was happy she made a *chitter, chitter* sound. When she was unhappy, she made a very loud, high, sharp sound like *klee klee*. She used her high screechy call to let Debbie know when she was hungry or wanted attention.

One day, Grandpa Stanley, who always wore a hat, came to visit. Bosley started screaming so loud that the neighbors called to see what was wrong. Bosley just kept screaming and looking at Grandpa. What was wrong with Bosley? Finally, Debbie said, "Gramps, take off your hat." He did, and the screaming stopped.

When Bosley outgrew the cage, arrangements were made for a neighbor to build a small aviary next to the house. Bosley made a nest in her new home and soon started

laying eggs. After laying four or five, she began sitting on her clutch. She sat and she sat. Over a month went by with Bosley faithfully sitting on her eggs. Poor Bosley! She had no way of knowing the eggs would never hatch because they weren't fertile.

Debbie felt sorry for her, so she went to a local bird farm and bought some dove eggs for Bosley to sit on. She patiently sat on those eggs for what seemed like forever. Then one day, Bosley's baby doves began to hatch. Bosley tried to be a good mother, but no one told her that the birds she hatched weren't sparrow hawks. Bosley just figured the babies would eat what she ate, so she would pick up a piece of meat and stuff it in the tiny dove's beak. When it wouldn't go down, Bosley tried to help by pushing a little harder. Her intentions were good, but she just didn't know any better, and ended up choking all of her poor little babies to death. And once more, she was alone.

Soon after that, Debbie decided it was time to teach Bosley how to be a wild bird, so she would open the door of the aviary and wait for Bosley

to fly away. But Bosley refused to budge. "Why won't Bosley fly away?" she asked the lady at the bird farm.

The lady replied, "Bosley thinks you're her mother and she doesn't want to leave you!"

Next, Debbie began to leave the door of the aviary open all the time, hoping Bosley would be curious and leave. One day, Debbie was in the house when she heard Bosley screaming in a sharp, shrill shriek at the top of her lungs. Debbie ran outside and found a cat was in the aviary trying to catch Bosley.

More than anything, Debbie wanted Bosley to be able to live a life in the wild, to find a mate, and raise babies. So she began having little chats with Bosley. "Bosley, you are a beautiful, big bird now. You can fly. Please fly outside and see what wonderful things God has for you." Patiently, she began to coax Bosley outside the aviary. At first she flew to the eucalyptus tree and then back again. The next day, she flew to the tree, then the telephone pole, and then back home for some mice. Each day, Bosley flew a little farther and stayed away a little longer. She kept increasing the time she was away until she was gone for over a month. When she returned, she was so weak that she could hardly stand. After eating enough to gain her strength, Bosley flew away again—and this time she didn't return for several months.

Once in a while, especially when Debbie was outside, she would hear Bosley's chittering call and look up and see her sitting on the telephone pole or in the branches of the eucalyptus tree. Debbie would talk to her for a while and then Bosley would fly away. At times, Bosley even followed Debbie over to her uncle's house, chittering all the way, but she never again landed on Debbie's shoulder or allowed Debbie to feed her.

Months later, Debbie was inside and heard Bosley's chittering call. She ran outside and saw Bosley sitting on the telephone pole with another sparrow hawk beside her. She had found a mate.

Many months went by and once again, Debbie heard Bosley's call. There she was sitting on the telephone pole with two little sparrow hawks beside her. It was almost as if she were saying, "Hi Debbie, meet my family. See, I do know how to be a good mother after all!" ■

> So don't be afraid; you are more valuable to
> God than a whole flock of sparrows.
> —Matthew 10:31, NLT

Angels Go Camping

Rhonda felt a nudge on her leg. "Leave me alone," she snapped at her younger sister. "I'm trying to sleep."

"La-la-la-la-la!" Kelli teased as her fingers crept within an inch of Rhonda's leg, before nudging her again.

Kelli was bored! She'd run out of things to do. Her favorite doll . . . ho-hum! Her new storybook . . . nah! Puzzles . . . yuck! Kelli was sure she'd been riding in the car for an eternity! *What's the fun of going on a camping trip if all you do is ride in the car?* she thought. In the front seat, Mom and Dad chatted amiably, leaving Rhonda as Kelli's only distraction.

"Stop it!" Rhonda hissed. "I'm trying to sleep!"

Kelli smirked and jiggled with silent laughter.

When Rhonda closed her eyes once more, Kelli's fingers crept across the great divide. This time, Rhonda sensed her fingers coming. *Slap!* Rhonda grinned at her little sister. Kelli slapped back. A volley of snappy slaps followed until Rhonda slapped hard enough to make Kelli's hand sting.

"Ouch! Rhonda hit me!" Kelli whined.

Mom whirled about in the seat. "Look, girls, I know you're tired of riding, but we're almost to the campground. See, there's the entrance!"

Dad eased the car onto the park's gravel road. "I hope we can find a decent campsite. It won't be easy, since it's the middle of summer vacation."

The girls exchanged looks of horror. If they didn't find a site at this campground, they'd have to ride to another, and then another, and then another . . .

"Help me spot a good campsite," Mom suggested. Eagerly, the girls pasted their faces to their windows.

"What's going on here?" Dad slowly drove through the park. "This place is empty, except for that one trailer at the top of the hill."

"Look! A playground!" Kelli shouted. "Can we camp here?"

"Sure, why not? It looks like we can camp anywhere we'd like."

Mom craned her neck about to check out the terrain. "I don't like the looks of this," she mumbled. "This place should be crawling with campers."

Dad stopped the car beside the lone trailer. An older couple was breaking camp, not setting up. Dad hopped out of the car and strode over to where the couple stood.

Rhonda leaned across the seat. "Mom, can we go play on the swings?"

"I guess so, for a few minutes anyway, until we know what we're doing."

Kelli and Rhonda leaped out of the car and dashed across the narrow roadway to the playground before Mom could change her mind.

"I'll beat you to the slide!" Rhonda shouted as she easily raced past her sister. By the time Rhonda climbed to the top of the slide, Dad had finished visiting with the people breaking camp and was talking with Mom.

"Look." Rhonda pointed to their parents. "That doesn't look good."

"So don't look at them," Kelli suggested as she waited her turn to go down the slide.

Swoosh! Down the silver slide Rhonda went. *This has to be the fastest slide in the entire world,* she thought. Her feet had barely touched the sawdust at the bottom when Kelli shouted, "Watch out! I'm coming!"

Again and again, the girls took turns going down the slide. Then they checked out the swings. As Rhonda hopped onto a swing she saw her father backing their trailer into a campsite. *That's good,* she thought. *We must be staying.*

Rhonda threw her head back and pumped the swing as high as she could go. It seemed like they'd barely played at all before Mom called, "Time to eat!"

Mealtime was usually filled with laughter, silliness, and good food, but not this time. Both Dad and Mom were very quiet. The girls exchanged worried glances with one another as they wound saucy spaghetti strands around their forks.

After dinner, Rhonda and Kelli helped Mom do the dishes, and then Dad gave the girls fifteen minutes longer to play before bedtime. The sun touched the mountain peaks to the west when he called them for family worship. "There's a reason no one is camping in this park," Dad began. "Last night every campsite was full until a gang of motorcyclists drove into the park, made lots of noise, overturned a couple of trailers, and threatened to hurt the campers. This morning the campers left and found rooms in local motels." The girls listened wide-eyed as Dad told them why the park was so empty.

"I don't like it here." Kelli glanced at the shadows of night developing among the big trees in the campground. "I wanna stay in a motel too."

"We can't, honey." Mom put her arms around her daughter. "First, all the motels are probably full. Second, we don't have the money to stay in a motel all weekend."

"We could drive to another campground." Rhonda hoped her suggestion would not be taken seriously.

"That's a good idea, princess." Dad tugged on her ponytail. "Except the closest campground is one hundred fifty miles away." Mom and the girls groaned aloud at the idea of driving any farther.

"There's a promise in God's Word that I believe perfectly fits our situation." Dad opened his Bible. "Let's see. It's right here, Psalm 34:7, 'The angel of the Lord encamps all around those who fear Him, and delivers them.' "

"Oh, I like that." Mom's eyes brightened. "Hey, if we could see our angels camping around us tonight, I wonder what it would look like?"

"I think they are camping in little white tents circling our trailer and car," Rhonda suggested.

Mom glanced at Kelli. "How do you picture the angel camp?"

Kelli giggled. "Maybe the angels are riding in covered wagons like the pioneers of the old west. They've circled the wagons around our trailer to protect us."

"I like that picture too," Mom admitted. "Either way, those beautiful, shining

angels can keep a puny little biker gang from bothering us, don't you think?"

After prayer, Dad closed his Bible. "OK, it's getting late. After such a long ride, you girls should sleep well tonight."

"Yeah." Rhonda yawned and stretched. "I'm pretty tired." She stretched again and winked at her sister. "Aren't you sleepy, Kelli?"

"Oh, yes." Kelli imitated her sister. "I can hardly wait to go to bed tonight."

The girls kissed their parents good night and ran into the trailer. For a time, Mom and Dad sat at the picnic table outside the trailer talking about the day's events. Inside, the girls had settled down, each with a good book and a flashlight. Every few minutes, one of the girls would peek out between the blinds to see if Mom and Dad were still talking.

"They're walking down the hill to that little lake," Rhonda whispered.

Kelli popped up and peered out of the same slat of blinds. The lake, not more than a hundred yards from the campsite, looked dark and frightening.

"I'm a little scared," Kelli admitted.

"Aw, come on scaredy-cat. Just read your book." Rhonda picked up her book and began to read aloud when the deafening sound of motorcycles roared up behind the trailer.

"Hey, look what we have here!" one of the motorcyclists shouted, revving his engine.

Terrified, Rhonda pulled apart the slats of the blinds at the rear window and looked out at a scruffy-faced man with a mustache, wearing dark sunglasses, and smoking a cigarette. He wore a black, sleeveless shirt with a scary-looking skeleton on the front, and a leather jacket with all sorts of pins, badges, and patches attached to it. His arms were covered with tattoos and he had a "don't mess with me or you're going to die" expression on his face. His companions didn't look any friendlier.

"I'm scared," Kelli wailed.

When another biker shook the trailer, Rhonda and Kelli both dived to the side window and yanked open the blinds looking for their parents.

Sure enough, both Mom and Dad were running toward the trailer.

"Mom!" Rhonda gasped. "Dad! Hurry!"

Horrified, the girls watched as their father called out, "May I help you, gentlemen?"

The girls raced to the back window in

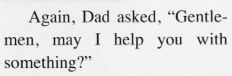

time to see the leader raise his hand. Instantly, his biking buddies stopped revving their engines. They stared at Dad, their eyes bulging with fear.

Again, Dad asked, "Gentlemen, may I help you with something?"

"Uh, uh," the leader stammered. "No, sir. No, sir! Come on guys," he shouted to the other bikers. "Let's get outta' here!"

The bikers revved their engines and squealed their tires as they disappeared out of sight.

Kelli and Rhonda bounded from the trailer and into their parents' outstretched arms.

"What did you do, Dad, to make those bad men go away?" Kelli whimpered.

"Nothing!" Dad looked stunned. "By the looks on their faces, you'd think they saw a division of armed policemen behind me."

"Maybe they did, Dad." Rhonda danced from one foot to the other. "Remember our angels? They could make themselves look like policemen or soldiers if they liked, couldn't they?"

Mom laughed. "You're right! They could."

"So I wonder, what they *did* see!"

Dad chuckled nervously. "Well, they saw something a whole lot more frightening than your mom or me, I can assure you."

"When we get to heaven," Kelli asked, "will Jesus show us what scared those men so much?"

"I hope so," Mom replied.

The next morning, as the family prepared to leave the campsite, a police car rolled up beside the trailer. The policemen asked about the biker gang and Dad told them what had happened.

His eyes narrowed with disbelief. "You don't expect me to believe that story, do you? Those are some dangerous guys!"

Dad shrugged. "That's what happened, officer."

The policeman shook his head, climbed back into his car, and left.

As they watched the patrol car drive away, Rhonda giggled. "I guess he's never heard of angels who go camping!" ∎

> *The angel of the LORD encamps all around those who fear Him, and delivers them.*
> —Psalm 34:7, NKJV

Late for School

66 "Hurry up, Michael. Put on your snow pants and coat. You're going to be late for school. And don't forget your hat. You'll want to play outside at recess." Mother grabbed the car keys and her purse. Outside their home in Lexington, Massachusetts, the thermometer registered twenty-eight degrees. And the wind whipping through the trees made it even colder.

"Come on. We have to hurry. Don't forget your lunch." Before Michael could zip up his jacket, his mother added, "Did you remember to put your homework in your backpack?"

Michael shrugged his shoulders and made a face. "No, I can't find it." He hated to be hurried. And this morning he hated having to rush even more. Grandma was visiting from Tennessee. She was staying home with his little brother, Jason, while he had to go to school. Somehow it didn't seem fair that Jason got to spend the whole day at home with Grandma!

Michael leaving for school.

Michael loves hugs from Grandma.

"Look on the dining room table where you left it last night," Mom called.

Michael found his sheet of homework and stuffed it in his backpack, then shuffled slowly back to the kitchen where Grandma was sitting with Jason. As he passed the table, Grandma gave him a big hug and told him to have a good day at school. "Don't worry, honey. I'll play games with you when you get home this afternoon."

Michael's face lit up. After planting a big kiss on Grandma's cheek, he shuffled out to the car. Looking back over his shoulder, he spotted Grandma at the kitchen window. She was holding Jason. Both of them were waving. Michael paused and waved back.

His mother opened the driver's door and hopped inside. As Michael opened the back door, he paused and glanced around as if he were listening to something.

"Come on, Michael. You're going to be late for school."

Michael frowned. "But, Mom, I thought I heard a noise." His mother rolled down her window to listen. After a few seconds of silence, she said, "I don't hear anything. Come on, Michael. We have to hurry."

The boy's frown deepened. "But Mom, I thought I heard someone yelling for help."

Having already started the engine to warm up the car, Mom shifted it into park and stepped outside to listen. She didn't hear anything. She glanced about, but didn't see anything, either. Then she turned toward Michael and heaved an exasperated sigh. She wondered if Michael was stalling because he didn't want to go to school.

Suddenly Michael whirled about and yelled, "Mom, there it is again! Can't you hear it? Someone *is* yelling for help." Michael listened carefully for a few moments and then took off running toward their neighbor's house. As he bounded through the snowdrifts, he shouted over his shoulder, "Mom, I think it's Nana Cupp."

By now, Mom was close behind. As they got nearer to their neighbor's house, she gasped as she spotted her elderly neighbor lying on the cold steps of her front porch with nothing on but her nightgown.

When Nana Cupp saw Michael and Mom running toward her, she cried out with relief. "Oh, thank you, thank you. I thought I was going to die."

Michael and his mother quickly helped her into the house. Michael talked softly and tenderly to her while his mother called 911. After the paramedics checked her over and found nothing seriously wrong, Nana Cupp explained that she had stepped out onto her porch to get the morning newspaper, and when she bent over to pick it up, she lost her balance and fell. Once down, she couldn't get up. "I called and called but no one heard me. How did you find me?" She looked at Mom. "How did you ever hear me calling? I was sure I was going to die right there!"

Michael with his mom, Rebecca Lynn.

Michael's mother shook her head. "I didn't hear you," she said, "but Michael did. When he said he heard someone calling for help I didn't believe him. I thought he was just stalling because he didn't want to go to school. But he kept insisting he heard something."

Nana Cupp took Michael's hand in hers and kissed it. "Oh Michael, you are a hero! I would have certainly froze to death out there in the cold. How can I ever thank you?"

Suddenly feeling shy, Michael looked at the grateful woman, "Nana Cupp, you don't have to thank me. I'm just glad Jesus used me to help you!"

The woman broke into a big smile. "Well, He certainly did that, my boy. He did that indeed! Jesus used you to save my life. You will always be my hero!"

Michael was late for school that morning, but that was all right with Mom and his teacher. And Michael felt good knowing that because he paused to listen, God had used him to save Nana Cupp's life. ∎

> *The LORD came and stood there, calling as at the other times, "Samuel! Samuel!"*
> *Then Samuel said, "Speak, for your servant is listening."*
> —1 Samuel 3:10, NIV

Joke on Mama

K̲ara stuffed the last bite of her peanut butter sandwich into her mouth and gulped the remainder of her milk. She glanced at the clock and then at her plate. Even as she swallowed the last of her food, Kara could hear the shouts of the neighborhood children gathering to play hide-and-seek in their large backyard. Quickly putting her empty plate in the dishwasher, Kara raced out the back door to join her older brother, Alan, and her younger sister, Sharon, and their friends in the lively game.

As the golden sunset disappeared and the stars began to shine, one by one the neighborhood kids headed home, leaving nothing for Alan, Kara, and Sharon to do until their folks arrived home. Alan was in charge, so he decided they could stay outside a little longer.

While they discussed what they might do with their extra free time, Mr. Porter, the man whose house was directly behind theirs, drove into the

alleyway hauling a small fishing boat. The vehicle stopped, and Mr. Porter and his teenage son, David, climbed out.

"Hey, Mr. Porter." Alan ran over to the chain link gate that separated their yard from the alleyway. "Catch anything?"

"Sure did! Come take a look."

Alan unlocked the gate and dashed across the narrow alleyway to the parked boat. Sharon and Kara bounded after him. Mr. Porter proudly held each fish up for the children to admire.

"Ooh! That's a big one!" Kara reached out to touch the scales of the last fish in the bucket. The fish felt smoother than it looked.

A wicked grin crossed David's face. "Look at what else we caught." David reached into a woven fishing basket and hauled out a four-foot-long black snake.

"Yikes!" Sharon and Kara jumped away from the side of the truck.

"Oh, don't worry. It's dead," David announced.

Kara shivered in fear. "I don't care if it's dead. I don't like it!"

"Me either!" Sharon cowered behind her sister.

"Hey, I think it's cool." Alan inched closer. "May I touch it?"

"Sure, help yourself," Mr. Porter laughed.

Alan touched the snake's side and then its head. He picked up the snake and wriggled the creature's body back and forth as if it were alive.

Kara shuddered. "Dead or not, the snake looks creepy. What are you going to do with it, Mr. Porter?"

"Toss it in the garbage, I suppose. Not much use for a dead snake."

Mr. Porter turned toward his son. "David, please take the fish to the garage and begin cleaning them."

"Sure, Dad." The boy grabbed the bucket from the back of the boat and headed for the garage.

Alan stared at the snake in his hands. "It's really creepy. If you're going to throw it away, may I have it?"

"Gross! No!" Sharon backed farther away.

"Aww, come on. It won't hurt you. Please, Mr. Porter?" Alan coaxed.

"Sure, go ahead. It's all yours." Mr. Porter laughed again, picked up his fishing gear and headed for his garage.

"Wow!" Alan's eyes glistened with excitement as he headed for their backyard. "What a find!"

Kara nodded in agreement and ran to keep up with her big brother. Sharon walked a few steps behind the other two.

"Come on, Sharon," Kara teased. "Don't be a scaredy-cat. It can't hurt you. It's dead!"

"I-I-I don't know . . ." Sharon eyed the snake's limp body draped across Alan's hands.

"Can I hold 'em? Please! Please!" Kara's heart raced. Though the snake still looked creepy, she wanted to appear braver than her sister.

"Sure." Alan dropped the snake onto Kara's hands. She screamed and leaped away. The creature fell to the ground.

"Eeewh! Throw it away!" Kara squealed, her face contorted in disgust.

"Yes! Throw it away!" Sharon agreed.

Alan laughed and bent down to pick up the snake. "Here, Sharon, you take it!"

"No!" Sharon whirled about and ran toward the house.

"Oh, don't be a sissy. I won't throw it at you." Alan cradled the dead snake on his arm.

"You'd better not or I'll tell Mama!" Sharon yelled as she kept her distance.

With the snake under her brother's control, Kara grew braver. "What are you going to do with it? You can't keep it forever."

Alan sat down on the grass and eyed the snake for a minute or two. "Let's scare someone."

"Who?" Kara asked, squatting down beside her brother. "All the kids have gone home for the night."

A glint came into Alan's eyes. "I know who. Mama hates snakes! Let's scare Mama."

"I don't think that's a good idea." Sharon inched closer.

"Aw, come on. It's not as if it's alive and might hurt her." Alan rose to his feet and headed toward the house. "It's just a joke. Where should we put it?"

The three children walked through the kitchen and then the dining room. "We could put it in the middle of the table," Alan suggested.

"Yuck! No way!" Kara wrinkled her nose. "We have to eat breakfast there."

"OK, how about in the living room? On the piano keys?" Sharon warmed to the adventure. "When Mama sits down to play for worship tonight, she'll find it."

Alan shook his head. "Not good enough. What if she doesn't play the piano tonight? I want to put it where she can't miss seeing it."

"In the bathroom?" Kara suggested.

"Yeah, I guess. Wait!" Alan stopped in the hallway outside their parents' bedroom. "How about on Mama's pillow? We could pull back the bedspread, put the snake on the pillow, and then pull the bedspread over the snake. That way, when she opens her bed, she can't miss seeing it."

"Good idea!" Kara giggled as she followed her brother into their parents' bedroom. "This is going to be so funny!"

Alan pulled back the bedspread and laid the snake on their mother's snowy white pillowcase. Kara adjusted the bedspread over the snake so that no one could tell the creature was there. Then they trooped down to the living room to wait for their parents to return home.

"I can't wait to see the look on her face when she sees that snake!" Alan laughed. "Mama is going to be *soooo* scared."

"Yeah, *soooo* scared . . ." Sharon mumbled, although she was starting to feel uneasy about their plan.

The longer they waited for their parents to return home, the less the three children talked about their great adventure. Kara thought about the snake and about her mother's reaction. She wondered how she'd feel if she found a dead snake on her pillow. *Maybe placing a dead snake on Mama's pillow isn't such a good idea,* she thought.

Thirty minutes passed. Kara felt less and less comfortable with their joke idea. A little voice was whispering in her head, *Not a good idea! Not a good idea!* Finally, she said, "Maybe we should call Dad and tell him about our joke."

"I think we should too." Sharon nodded.

"Yeah. You may be right." Alan tapped in the numbers for their father's cell phone and waited. "Dad? No, we're all OK. Don't worry, nothing's wrong. I just wanted to ask you a question."

Alan told their father the entire story about the joke they planned to pull on their mother and then listened to their father's reply.

"Uh, yeah. No. Yes. Uh, right. Probably so. Yeah, OK. I got it. Thanks, Dad," Alan mumbled.

"What did he say? What did he say?" Kara urged.

Slowly, Alan hung up the phone and placed it back in its cradle. "He didn't like our idea of a joke.

He said we have to take the snake off the pillow before they get home."

"Was he mad?" Sharon timidly asked.

"No." Alan heaved a deep sigh and started toward their parents' room. "I guess our joke wasn't such a good idea after all."

"Did you just figure that out?" Sharon huffed. "I knew it was a bad idea all along!"

Kara whipped about to face her sister. "Then why didn't you say so?"

"Nobody asked," she said as she stomped off.

After removing the snake from their mother's pillow and remaking the bed, the three children went back to the living room to await their parents' arrival. Alan placed the dead snake in the middle of the living room floor and they sat around it in a circle.

"I'm glad we called Dad about the snake on Mama's pillow," Kara admitted. "At first, I thought it would be a funny joke, but the longer we waited the less funny it became."

"Yeah, I know what you mean," Alan nodded in agreement. "I think I knew deep down inside that it wasn't such a good joke to play on Mama."

At the sound of the garage door opening and their parents' car pulling into the driveway, Alan and his sisters ran to the kitchen door. Even though Dad had prepared Mama for the sight of the dead snake on her living room floor, she shivered at the sight of it. *What if Mama gets angry? What if she grounds us for even considering pulling such a joke,* Kara wondered.

Mama's voice shook as she calmly said, "Alan, please throw that creature in the garbage can . . . *Now!*"

Immediately, Alan scooped up the snake and disappeared out the kitchen door.

"Oh, Mama," Kara dashed into her mother's arms. "We're so sorry. I guess scaring you with that snake would have been kinda mean. Inside, I knew it wasn't such a good idea. Sharon knew it too. She never really wanted to go along with it."

Mama patted Kara on the head. "It wouldn't have made me very happy, for sure. I'm so glad you listened to the voice inside of you and called to ask Dad about it."

Sharon hopped onto her father's lap as he sank into his giant recliner.

"Playing harmless jokes on people is fun," Dad explained, "but you have to know when a joke stops being a joke and becomes a mean

prank. Listening to the voice inside that warns you when you're about to do something foolish will keep you out of a lot of trouble."

"And it will make everyone a lot happier." Sharon added.

"That's right!" Dad kissed her on the cheek. Sharon snuggled further into her father's arms and giggled, "Jesus will be happier too." ■

> *My sheep hear My voice, and I know them,*
> *and they follow Me.*
> —John 10:27, NKJV

Mishanda's Missing Money

Mishanda sang to herself as she skipped along the sidewalk on her way to the Kims' house. They had a younger son named John, and Mishanda often stopped to play with him. The Kims were a nice family, and their home reflected that they probably had more money than Mishanda's family. That didn't bother her at all. She was made to feel welcome and often stopped in just to talk. Mishanda's parents had met the Kims and knew that she was safe visiting with them.

Mishanda loved to look at all the lovely things the Kims had brought with them from their homeland of China: vases in rich blues, silks that covered the pillows, and little statues that sat on their bookcases. But most of all, Mishanda loved to play with their cat, a beautiful Siamese named Luna. Mishanda laughed out loud when she found out the name was short for Lunatic.

John and Mishanda were playing on the wide front porch when Mrs.

Kim came out carrying a pitcher of lemonade and some tall glasses.

"You guys thirsty yet?" Mrs. Kim set the tray down on a small table and poured each of them a drink. Mishanda and John sat on the steps, sipping ice-cold lemonade.

"*Mmm,* this tastes so good. Thank you." Mishanda smiled at Mrs. Kim.

"You are most welcome." Mrs. Kim watched Mishanda. She seemed to be studying her as if she were thinking about something.

"Mishanda," Mrs. Kim finally spoke, "we have a problem, and I'm wondering if you could help us out."

"I will, if I can," Mishanda replied.

"We're going on vacation next week, and we are having a hard time finding a place to board Luna and her three kittens. We hate to take her away from her home since her babies are still so young. Do you think you would be able to come over and feed and water Luna for us while we are gone?"

"I'd love to do that. I'll ask my parents if it's OK." Mishanda grinned at Mrs. Kim.

"Of course, we will pay you."

"Oh, you wouldn't have to do that. I love Luna."

"Yes, but this would be a real job. You would have to come twice a day. You couldn't miss any of the times. It's a lot of responsibility."

"I can do it, I'm sure. You can trust me." All of a sudden, Mishanda felt very big.

Mishanda was so excited when her parents gave their permission for her to take care of Luna and her babies.

The Kims had shown her where they kept Luna's food and how to measure it out to make sure she got all she needed. They showed her the litter box and how to scoop it out to keep it clean. She watched as Luna tucked her fluffy babies close to her, and she remembered that she shouldn't play much with the tiny kittens since they were so young. They looked funny with their eyes still sealed shut, but Mishanda knew that someday they would be just as beautiful as their mother.

A week later, Mishanda was on her way to her first real job and was

thrilled that the Kims had trusted her to do it. She thought about the money she would earn. First, she planned to give her tithe to God. She always wanted to please her heavenly Father. Then, she knew that she would also give an offering. God was so good, she wanted to say a special big thanks. Then she made a mental list of all the things she could buy . . . and before she knew it, she stood in front of the Kims' door.

Mishanda put the key in the lock and turned it. She pushed open the door and walked into the beautiful room. Luna meowed when she saw Mishanda and came to rub herself against her leg. She bent down to scratch the cat behind her ear.

"Food's on the way, Luna."

The cat followed Mishanda into the kitchen and watched intently as she did her job. After cleaning out the litter box, Mishanda looked around to make sure everything was in place, then pulled the door shut and locked it.

Mishanda's Missing Money

The two weeks went faster than Mishanda had imagined. It had rained on several of the days. She didn't feel like going out in bad weather, but she knew she had a job to do and that Luna and her family were counting on her.

One day, there was a surprise waiting for Mishanda. The Kims' van was in the driveway, so she knocked on the door instead of letting herself in.

"Mishanda, you've done such a nice job. Come in." Mrs. Kim smiled as she pushed open the door. "Luna looks well cared for. And thanks for keeping things picked up. I'm so pleased with your work."

Mishanda smiled. She felt good knowing that what she had done was appreciated.

"Let me get my purse." Mrs. Kim walked into her bedroom and came back with two bills in her hand. "This is for you."

"Oh, Mrs. Kim, forty dollars is way too much."

"Listen, Mishanda. You deserve every bit of it. You did an excellent job. What do you plan on doing with your money?"

"Well, first I'm going to give God my tithe, which is ten percent. And then I'll give an offering at church, then . . ."

"You are going to give some of your money to God?" Mrs. Kim looked like she didn't understand.

"Yes. God asks that we give Him back some of what we earn, and I've always tried to do that. It's one of His special promises, that if we honor Him, He will bless us. Then, I like to give an offering that comes from my heart."

"That's nice, Mishanda, but you don't get money just for yourself too often. Don't you want to buy some special things?"

"There will be plenty left. God always takes care of me." Mishanda smiled at Mrs. Kim.

"I can't say I understand, Mishanda. But I think you are a very wise young lady. I need to go to the store. Would you like to ride with me and pick out some things to buy with your money?"

"Oh, thank you. Can I call my mom to make sure it's OK?"

"Of course!"

Twenty minutes later they were at the store, and Mishanda reached into her pocket to get her money, only this time . . . it wasn't there!

"Oh, no!"

"What's wrong?" Mrs. Kim looked worried.

"My money! It's gone!"

"What do you mean, Mishanda?"

"I put it here in my pocket, but it must have fallen out."

Mishanda and Mrs. Kim looked everywhere. They retraced their steps in the store and looked in the van. They couldn't find the money anywhere. Mrs. Kim drove back to her home and helped Mishanda look inside the house where she had given her the money.

"It's gone," Mishanda said, trying hard not to cry.

"I'm sorry. You worked so hard for it."

"I know what to do. Let's pray," Mishanda suggested.

"Pray? I don't understand. How will that help?" Mrs. Kim frowned.

"God hears our prayers. He will help us find the money," Mishanda said confidently.

"OK. You go ahead." Mrs. Kim bowed her head and listened as Mishanda talked to God like He was her Friend. It seemed very different to her than other prayers she had heard.

Mishanda said "Amen" but kept her head bowed for a few seconds. She was adding a prayer that Mrs. Kim would see how wonderful God really was.

Mishanda slowly raised her head and looked up. Mrs. Kim had a funny look on her face.

"I think I know where your money might be." Mishanda quickly followed Mrs. Kim outside and watched as she moved around the rocks that lined her driveway. Suddenly, a flash of green appeared next to one of the rocks.

"Mishanda, come quickly." She bent down and brushed away some leaves, uncovering the missing money!

With a big smile on her face, Mrs. Kim handed the bills to Mishanda.

"How did you know, Mrs. Kim?"

"Well, when you were praying, the thought came to me that you might have dropped them when you were getting into the van, and the wind could have blown them against the rocks. Do you think your God used me to answer your prayer?"

"I know He did, Mrs. Kim. Isn't God wonderful?" Mishanda beamed.

Mrs. Kim looked very thoughtful. "You know, Mishanda, I'm beginning to think He is."

It would have been hard to say who had the brightest smile at that moment, Mrs. Kim, Mishanda, or their loving God who watched from heaven. ■

> *"Bring all the tithes into the storehouse . . .*
> *and try Me now in this," says the* LORD *of hosts,*
> *"If I will not open for you the windows of*
> *heaven and pour out for you such blessing that*
> *there will not be room enough to receive it."*
> —Malachi 3:10, NKJV

Matthew's Test

"What's this?" Matthew asked, taking the paper Isaiah held out to him.

"It's the answers to the math test tomorrow," Isaiah whispered.

"What? Where did you get them?" Matthew frowned.

Isaiah looked around to make sure no one was listening. "I copied the answers out of Mrs. Carlson's book while she was out of the room," he snickered.

Matthew glanced at the paper and stuffed it into his back pocket, while Isaiah began handing the answer sheets to other classmates.

When Matthew got home, he tossed his backpack next to his bed. Since he wouldn't need to study for the math test, he would have time to level-up on his computer game.

"Matthew, you need to get off the computer and study for your math test,"

Mom reminded.

"It will be an easy test." Matthew felt guilty for lying to his mom, so he kept his eyes on his game.

"No games until you study," Mom said. "You know the rule."

"All right!" Matthew shut off the computer and got out his math book. The more he thought about cheating and lying to his mom, the more his stomach churned. He knew it was wrong, and he didn't like how he felt just thinking about it.

He took a deep breath. *I guess I had better study,* he said to himself.

That night during worship, Matthew had a hard time listening to the Bible story. His thoughts were back at school, Isaiah, and the math test. *What was Isaiah thinking stealing the answers? How many kids will cheat? Will*

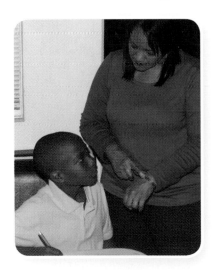

they all get into trouble? The more he thought about what would be happening the next day, the more he resolved to prove to himself that he could ace the test honestly. As soon as prayer was over, Matthew once more got out his math book and studied each section over and over again until he was sure he was ready for the test.

It was late when Mom came to check on him. "Matthew, I can't believe you're still studying. I was afraid you would already be asleep and I had missed tucking you in. Close your book now," she said as she bent over and kissed his forehead.

"OK." Matthew dropped his math book into his backpack and climbed into bed.

Mom turned off the light and then stopped in the doorway. "I'm proud of you for studying so hard."

Matthew smiled and pulled up the blankets. *I'm glad that Mom is proud of me. But would she be if she knew how close I came to cheating? Why did I even take the answer sheet? I should have said NO immediately.* He felt guilty that he had even considered it.

The next morning, Matthew wasn't very hungry and he was really tired. He had tossed and turned a lot during the night thinking about the test and what Isaiah and the other students were planning to do. *Should I tell on Isaiah? I don't like tattle-tales. What should I do?*

"You'll do better on your test if you eat breakfast," Mom reminded.

By the time Matthew managed to force down a few bites of oatmeal, he had made a decision. He would do his best on the test and not worry about the others. If they chose to cheat, they would just be hurting themselves. He grabbed his backpack and hurried down the sidewalk to school.

Math was the last period of the day. The hours dragged by. When

at last it was time for class, Matthew felt sick to his stomach. Mrs. Carlson came into the room. "Cory, please put away your books. Nothing should be on your desk except your test paper and pencil," she instructed.

"Yes, ma'am," Cory answered.

Isaiah turned around and grinned at Matthew, but Matthew avoided eye contact and didn't smile back.

"Turn around, Isaiah," Mrs. Carlson said in a stern voice.

The last thing Matthew needed was to get in trouble for cheating when he had chosen not to. Suddenly, he thought of something that made his stomach feel like a rock. He couldn't remember where he had put the answer sheet Isaiah had given to him. He touched his sweatshirt pocket to see if it might be there, but it felt empty. He breathed a sigh of relief. At least he wouldn't get in trouble for having the answers on him. Before starting the test, Matthew said a little prayer. *Dear Jesus, please help me to pass the test. And please forgive me for even thinking about cheating. Amen.* Matthew took a deep breath and began working through the problems.

It wasn't long before Isaiah took his paper to Mrs. Carlson and left the room. Then a few more students did the same.

Matthew tried to think about the math problems and nothing else. When he was finally finished, he stood up. As he took his test to Mrs. Carlson, he noticed the room was empty. "I guess I should have studied harder. I'm the last to finish," Matthew said.

"You finished on time. That's all that matters." Mrs. Carlson smiled.

Matthew walked into the hall and headed toward his locker.

"What took you so long?" Isaiah asked. "It was an easy A."

Matthew shrugged his shoulders, walked past Isaiah, and left school without saying anything. His mind was mulling over the whole situation. *Should I have told Mrs. Carlson about all the students that had cheated?* These were his friends. He didn't want them to get into trouble, but he wished that they would learn that it doesn't pay to cheat.

At home, Mom was waiting for him. "Matthew, I want to talk to you about your math test."

"Sure, Mom," Matthew said, removing his backpack from his shoulders.

"I found this in the pocket of your jeans," Mom said, handing him the paper with the test answers.

Matthew sighed and looked at his sneakers. "It's the answers to the math test today, but I didn't use it. I've never cheated and I don't want to start now."

"I'm proud of you," Mom said as she bent down and kissed his forehead.

"I'm not," Matthew said.

"Why not?" Mom asked. "You said you didn't cheat."

"I didn't, but I was tempted. I wanted to play computer games instead of studying. That's why I told you the test was going to be easy. But the more I thought about it, the worse I felt. Finally, I decided it was better to study and have a clear conscience than to cheat and feel miserable! But I came so close! What if I had cheated?" Matthew asked.

"You didn't, and that's what counts," Mom said.

The next day, Mrs. Carlson walked into math class looking very unhappy. "Before I give your tests back, I have something to say. The test scores were unsettling. Only five people passed and only a few students showed their work. It makes me think that most of you didn't study. Homework is important if you want to do well in school. It's your responsibility, whether or not your parents remind you. Now get out your books and go over your test material. Those who failed will be given another exam with similar problems. I want to make sure you know this material before going on." Then Mrs. Carlson began handing out the graded tests.

Isaiah turned around and confidently grinned at Matthew as he

whispered, "Well, at least *we* passed!" But Matthew didn't want to look at him. It made him think about cheating.

"No talking, please," Mrs. Carlson said.

When Mrs. Carlson came to Matthew, she smiled. "Good job, Matthew."

Matthew couldn't believe his eyes. He got an A! He felt the weight of guilt lift off his shoulders. "Thank You, Jesus," Matthew whispered out loud.

"What's Jesus got to do with it?" Isaiah asked, turning around once again.

"Everything," Matthew answered quietly. "I studied—and didn't even look at the answer sheet! I prayed that Jesus would help me pass the test fair and square. And He did!"

After Mrs. Carlson gave Isaiah his test paper, Matthew heard him exclaim under his breath, "Guess I messed up on the answers."

That night, after he'd finished his homework, Matthew confided to his mom. "Only five students passed the math test and I was one of them. Do you know what that means?"

"It means you studied," Mom said.

"It means that almost everyone cheated," Matthew explained. "I've never seen Mrs. Carlson so upset."

"I'm proud of you," Mom said.

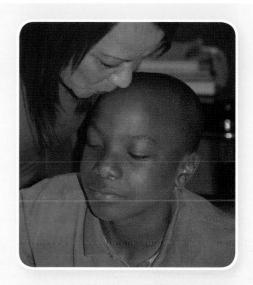

Matthew was proud of himself too. He was happy he hadn't cheated. He was thankful to Jesus for helping him to study hard and remember what he had learned. Right then, Matthew determined that he would never, ever cheat, regardless of how easy it might be. In fact, he wouldn't even be tempted to do so. He didn't need test answers. All he needed was Jesus. ■

Resist the devil and he will flee from you.
Draw near to God and He will draw near to you.
—James 4:7, 8, NKJV

Grandpa's Two Hearts

The sirens blared through the rush hour traffic on a busy Seattle street. Just a few minutes earlier, the 911 dispatcher had received a breathless call from an old man having a heart attack at the Shady Oaks Senior Community Center.

The ambulance arrived in record time and the EMTs jumped out, grabbed a stretcher, and raced to reach the downtown building. When they made it to apartment 237, they found a man weakly grasping the phone and slumped against a chair. Quickly, they placed him on the stretcher and rushed him to the hospital.

Just as he arrived in the emergency room, the old man's heart stopped.

"Stand back!" the doctor ordered his assistants, as he grabbed two big paddles.

Nurses ripped the man's shirt open just before the doctor placed the paddles on his chest. *ZAP!* The electricity from the paddles flowed into the man's body, shocking his heart into beating again.

The next thing the old man knew, as he slowly gained consciousness, was what the kind doctor was telling a nurse, "That man is lucky to be alive."

A few hours later, Mom's cell phone rang. It was the old man's neighbor. "What? Oh no! Do you know when he'll be able to return home?" Mom's voice began to break up and crackle. When she was through talking, she slowly placed her phone on the table by the couch.

"What's wrong, Mom? Is it Grandpa again?" Jonathan asked. He knew that his grandpa had a heart problem, and from Mom's end of the conversation, it didn't sound too good.

"Yes, honey," Mom replied as the tears ran freely down her face. "Grandpa's neighbor in Seattle just called to let me know that the ambulance came for him. He had a heart attack. They said that if he had arrived at the hospital just ten minutes later, he would have died. He has a lot of health problems, but his heart is the worst."

Jonathan thought about that for a long time. He knew that Grandpa had a bigger problem than just his heart. He drank too much alcohol. It had been hard for Jonathan's mom when she was growing up because sometimes the alcohol caused her father to get very angry. Sometimes he said and did things that hurt her. He was an unhappy, miserable man when he was drinking. He complained, blamed others, and spent far too much of his time just sitting in front of the TV rather than meeting people and enjoying the outdoors. As he got older and the kids all left home, he didn't get angry like he once did, but he still drank, and that had caused all kinds of health problems.

Regardless, Mom never stopped loving him and neither did Jonathan, even though Grandpa lived thousands of miles away. Jonathan and his mom and dad had prayed many times that God would help Grandpa not to drink. "Mom, is Grandpa still drinking?" Jonathan wondered.

"Well, I'm sure he's not drinking right now, because the hospital won't let him, but I don't know what he'll do when he gets out," Mom said with a tired sounding sigh as she wiped her tears.

Suddenly, Jonathan had an idea, "Mom, doesn't it say in the Bible that God will give us a new heart?"

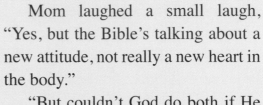

Mom laughed a small laugh, "Yes, but the Bible's talking about a new attitude, not really a new heart in the body."

"But couldn't God do both if He wanted to?" Jonathan persisted.

"God can do anything, son, but He doesn't ever force people. They have to want His help. They have to want to change."

"But couldn't we pray that Grandpa would want both kinds of a new heart, the one for his body and the one for his attitude?" Jonathan asked hopefully.

"Yes, we can ask God for anything," Mom said hesitantly, "but it will be Grandpa's choice to allow God to work in his life."

"Then, let's pray right now," Jonathan insisted.

And that's just what they did.

As soon as they were finished, Jonathan pleaded, "Let's call Grandpa and see if he has a new heart!"

"No, not right now," Mom replied. "He is in the intensive care unit and not able to talk on the phone. We'll call him later and see how he's doing."

The days seemed to go by slowly, but each morning and evening at family worship, Dad, Mom, and Jonathan prayed for Grandpa, claiming the promise in Ezekiel 36:26: "I will give you a new heart, and I will put a new spirit in you. I will take out your stony, stubborn heart and give you a tender, responsive heart."

Jonathan also prayed in his personal prayer time and whenever he thought about it during the day. Jonathan even got the people at church to pray for his grandpa to get a new heart and a new attitude.

Finally, after a week, Mom tried calling Grandpa's cell phone. Before, she had gotten only his voicemail. But this time, she heard Grandpa's voice on the other end. Even though he sounded weak, he was home. Mom was so surprised because he actually sounded happy! Not grumpy at all!

Mom talked to Grandpa for quite a while, and when she hung up the phone she was wiping tears of joy from her eyes.

"Well, tell us, how is Grandpa?" Jonathan asked eagerly.

"Yes, don't keep us hanging. Is he OK?" Dad asked.

"Yes, he is more than OK! He told me the whole story. You see, Grandpa was alone in his apartment when he felt his heart acting very strange. That's when he thought he was dying, so he called 911, and an ambulance came and took him to the hospital. After the doctors helped his heart to work again, they told him he was lucky to be alive. Instead of being happy, he was sad. He thought about his life and all the bad choices that alcohol had caused him to make and he didn't feel like living like that anymore."

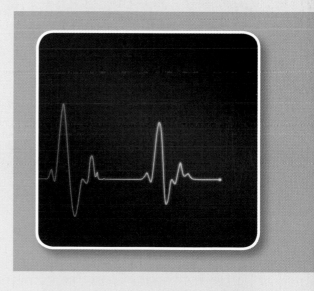

"Does Grandpa want to die?" Jonathan asked with concern.

"No," Mom replied, "he asked God to give him a new heart, and now he wants to live for Jesus!"

"Oh, Mom, I'm so glad Grandpa is going to live! And I'm even happier that he loves Jesus!" Jonathan exclaimed.

"Me too, son," Mom said, giving him a gentle hug.

"Grandpa needed a pacemaker to help his heart beat regularly, and since he was doing so well, the doctors released him from the hospital. Now that he is home, he looks at life differently. He is so happy to be alive! He loves his house. He loves his neighbors. He loves the sunshine! He just loves everything!"

"Are you talking about Grandpa? He's never happy about anything!" Jonathan exclaimed.

"Yes, I'm talking about your grandpa. Jesus gave him a new attitude with his new heart!" Mom said as she wiped her eyes again. "Now Grandpa feels happy inside, almost young again! Even though he lives alone, he doesn't feel lonely anymore!"

"We've been praying, Mom, that Grandpa wouldn't be lonely."

"Yes, Jonathan, and our prayers have been answered. Grandpa told me a funny story how a squirrel showed him how much Jesus loves him."

"A squirrel?" Jonathan asked.

"Yes, a squirrel. One day, not long after Grandpa got home from the hospital, he decided to wheel his wheelchair out onto the balcony of his apartment for some fresh air. Just then, a ray of sunlight pierced through the cloudy sky and made your grandpa smile. At the same time, a squirrel ran up the fire escape.

"Suddenly, the squirrel jumped onto his balcony. As you know, Grandpa usually has a pocket full of peanuts that he feeds to the squirrels, but since he had been in the hospital he didn't have a chance to shop, and the peanut jar was empty. All of a sudden, the usually shy squirrel did something amazing. It jumped right onto Grandpa's lap, looked into his

eyes, and grabbed his shirt with its paws as if it were saying, 'Hey, I need you!'

"Then it started digging in Grandpa's shirt pocket for peanuts. This made Grandpa laugh so hard his belly shook and the frightened squirrel ran away. Grandpa could hardly believe it! He thought about how awesome it was that God could send sunshine on a cloudy day and a squirrel to let him know he was loved!"

"Wow, that is so cool, Mom! I bet that made Grandpa feel really special."

"Yes, it did," Mom replied. "I don't think Grandpa ever realized just how special he is to Jesus!"

That night, when Jonathan went to bed, he had an extra long Thank-You prayer. As he knelt with his family to pray, he thanked God for the doctors who gave his grandpa a pacemaker that made his heart beat right again. But most of all, he thanked Jesus for coming into Grandpa's heart.

As Dad tucked him into bed, they talked about Grandpa and how different he was now. Jonathan sat up suddenly, "Hey, Dad, Jesus is so awesome! He didn't just fix one heart—God gave Grandpa TWO new hearts!" ■

> *And I will give you a new heart, and I will put*
> *a new spirit in you.*
> *I will take out your stony, stubborn heart and*
> *give you a tender, responsive heart.*
> —Ezekiel 36:26, NLT

MBBS2—5

Buried Treasure

"Hurry up, Holly!" Mom called. "If you're not careful, you'll miss your ride to school."

Holly's mind was on a hundred different things as she sauntered down the hall from her room.

"All ready, Mom," Holly said cheerfully.

"Did you brush your teeth?" Mom asked. Holly's face went blank for a second and then she shook her head.

Mom frowned and pointed to the bathroom. "Go."

"How about your backpack?" Mom shouted to Holly over the running water. "And those library books that are due?"

"Oh, yeah," Holly mumbled through her toothpaste-filled mouth. "I'll get them."

Holly's mom shook her head. "Honestly, I hope you start remembering things pretty soon. Sometimes it seems . . ." She was interrupted by a car horn.

"Your ride's here," said Mom as she opened the front door and waved. Holly grabbed her backpack and came back into the living room.

"Mom, why don't we get our car fixed so you can take me to school yourself?"

"This is why," said Mom as she held up a white envelope and gave it to Holly. "It's either get the car fixed or pay this month's tuition. Your Christian schooling is a lot more important to me than that car." She smiled at Holly. "Give this to the school secretary as soon as you get there, and please, please, don't lose it."

Holly smiled. "No problem. I'll put it in my math book. Math's my first subject. When I open it up, I'll remember to take it to the office." Holly waved as she left.

At the same time Holly was riding to school, a boy named Andrew sat alone on the school bus. Last evening he had heard his dad say, "I almost have enough money to get a new hard drive for my computer. This one isn't going to last much longer."

"How much does a hard drive cost, Dad?" Andrew asked. His dad owned his own business and Andrew knew that financially his family was struggling right now.

"Well, the one I need for work costs about three hundred dollars. I've been setting money aside each month and I only need one hundred more."

Now as Andrew sat on the school bus, he wondered, *Is there anything I can do to help Dad get the money he needs? He works so hard. Maybe I could get a job after school. I'll pray about it and see what happens.*

By now, Holly's ride had reached the drop-off area. As Holly bounced out of the car, she yelled across the playground to Britney, "Hey, we have ten minutes before the first bell rings. Wanna try the swings?"

Britney headed for the swings, with Holly running from the other direction. "First!" shouted Holly.

"Not!" Britney shouted, playfully shoving Holly with her shoulder, causing Holly's backpack to fall to the ground.

"Hey, careful!" Holly said as she gently shoved Britney back, "I'm delicate!" Their scuffling caused the sand to fly.

The girls played until the first bell rang a few minutes later. Holly scooped up her backpack that was half buried in the sand and ran with her friends to the classroom.

Fifteen minutes later Holly's teacher said, "Open your math books to page sixty-two."

Math book . . . Holly thought to herself. *There's something about the math book. What is it that's so important? I wonder if I forgot to do my assignment, but no . . . here it is right between the pages. Is there supposed to be something else between the pages? Oh no!* Suddenly, the light went on in her brain.

"I need to go to the office, please," Holly told her teacher, trying not to panic, as she grabbed her math book and raced to the office.

At the very same time Holly was heading to the office, Andrew's class was gathering outside getting ready to go on a field trip to the local bird sanctuary. As the class waited for the bus driver, Andrew and his friend, Ted, sat on the swings.

"Looks like it's going to be a while," Andrew complained. *Might as well get comfortable,* he thought. He loved the feeling of the sand on his feet, so he took a minute to take his shoes off, and then his socks. He slid his toes beneath the surface of the sand. *Oh, that feels good. But . . . what's this?* He suddenly felt something poking him between his toes.

Andrew reached down under the sand and pulled out a white envelope.

What's this—buried treasure? he said to himself. He opened the envelope and looked inside. It really was buried treasure! Andrew counted five crisp twenty-dollar bills. *This is the exact amount Dad needs to buy the new hard drive for his computer! It's an answer to my prayer . . . isn't it?*

Meanwhile, inside the office, Holly grew more and more panicky as she flipped through the pages of her math book. "It should be here somewhere," she said to the secretary, desperation in her voice.

"Maybe it's in your backpack," the secretary offered. Holly put down her math book and began digging through her backpack.

What will I do if I can't pay my tuition? she thought frantically. *Will they make me quit school?*

She continued searching for a few moments before looking at the secretary. "It's not here," she said finally. Tears welled up in her eyes.

"Now, don't panic," the secretary said. "Take everything out of your backpack, one item at a time. Go through it thoroughly."

Holly's mind whirled. *Where could the envelope be?*

Two hours later, Holly had still not found the money and was now sitting in the principal's office, sobbing. She had even retraced her steps all the way back to the swing set, but found nothing. Just the thought of having to tell her mom that she had lost the money sent fresh tears streaming down her cheeks. Miss Ramona, the principal, was trying to calm her down.

"Relax, Holly," she said. "Losing that money doesn't mean you're going to have to leave school. It was an accident. Anyone could make that mistake."

"But you don't understand," Holly sobbed. "Mom didn't get our car fixed so she could pay my tuition. How will she be able to pay it later if she could barely pay it this month?"

"We'll work something out," Miss Ramona said gently. "Holly, have you prayed about it?"

Holly sniffed. "A hundred times already. But nothing's happened."

Miss Ramona smiled again. "Well, I'm sure God has heard your prayers, but He doesn't always answer the way you expect."

"Miss Ramona, I'm sorry to interrupt," the secretary said, coming in from the outer office. "Andrew,

one of our students, says he would like to speak with you." She led Andrew into Miss Ramona's office.

"What can I do for you, Andrew?" the principal asked.

"Miss Ramona, I found something in the sand, and I need your advice."

"What do you mean, Andrew?" Miss Ramona asked.

"I prayed to God that He would help me find a way to earn money so my dad could buy a new hard drive, and then I found all this money in an envelope buried in the sand. It's the exact amount of money I prayed for. But then a voice told me that it might belong to someone else." He held up the white envelope as grains of sand fell onto the floor.

"My money!" Holly cried, and reached her hand out for it.

"Just a second," Miss Ramona said to Holly. "Andrew, you found that buried treasure fair and square. But Holly lost it this morning. That money is supposed to pay her tuition so she will be able to go to school here. What do you think you should do?"

"Well, my dad needs a new hard drive for his computer, but since this money belongs to Holly, it wouldn't be right for me to keep it." He stepped forward and gave the envelope to Holly, who grinned through a tear-soaked face. "Thank you, thank you!" she exclaimed.

Andrew didn't have the money for his dad's hard drive, but he had something much better; the happiness he felt inside because he did the right thing! ■

Therefore, whatever you want men to do to you, do also to them.
— Matthew 7:12, NKJV

Garden of Weedin'

"Ahh, there's nothing that tastes better than a juicy, sun-ripened tomato, right off the vine," Dad said, smacking his lips. "Someday, we'll have a garden that will grow all kinds of delicious vegetables, like tomatoes, green beans, and corn." Dad loved to share his dream with his sons, Steven and Daniel. But it seemed that wherever they moved on the big island of Hawaii, the soil was mostly lava—and lava caused the plants to be stunted due to lack of nutrients and moisture. "Yes, someday we'll find a place with rich soil where we can have our very own Garden of Eden."

Dad sold books for a living, but his main job was homeschooling Steven and Daniel. They especially enjoyed spending time on the sparkling black sand beach called Punalu'u where they would take their books and do their school work under a coconut palm and swim or snorkel for recess.

Just seven miles from Punalu'u Beach, on a road that went from sea level to 2,000 feet, Dad finally found his dream acreage. The farm was called Wood Valley. It was still tropical, but much cooler than the beach, and the land was watered with crystal pure water that flowed through a lava tube. The owner had built tiny cabins where workers could stay in exchange for just ten hours of farm work a week; a pretty sweet deal if you have two energetic boys—and not much money. And

best of all, there was plenty of land for Dad and his boys to have a large garden of their own, where the soil was perfect for growing vegetables.

So when summer rolled around and the school books were put away, Dad announced, "I've made arrangements with the owner to plow up some land for our garden." As the plow went back and forth turning over the soil, the boys shouted with excitement, "We're rich! We're rich! Look at that beautiful, black soil."

"When can we plant the seeds we've been saving?" Steven hounded his dad.

"Maybe in three weeks."

"Three weeks? Why can't we plant now?"

"Because," said Dad, "this ground is so fertile that the weeds are going to grow just as fast—or faster—than our vegetables. What we need to do first is pull out all the weeds that the plow has dug up and then wait a week. Chances are a new crop of weed seeds will have sprouted by then, and then we'll pull those."

"Then can we plant?" urged Daniel.

"Not yet," said Dad. "We've got to prepare the soil by pulling out all the weeds that might grow and choke out our seeds. So, we'll need to wait another week and pull up one more crop of weeds. Then I think the soil should be ready for planting."

The boys groaned. Planting sounded like fun; weeding sounded like work.

"Come on," Dad urged. "We've been talking about having a garden for months. We've got work to do! Grab a shovel or a pick and start pulling out anything green. Be sure you get the roots, and then throw them in a pile. Then we'll shovel the weed pile into the wheelbarrow and cart it away."

Suddenly, the sun was too hot, they were thirsty, their hands hurt, their jeans were getting dirty, or they were hungry. Those two boys thought up more excuses to try to get out of weeding the garden than anyone could imagine. But Dad was firm, "I know this seems like a lot of work, but God tells us that if we work hard, we will enjoy the fruits of our labor. Everything worthwhile takes a little effort. This soil is so rich that if we prepare the soil first, we'll end up with a much greater harvest. Come on, Steven, grab that shovel. And Daniel, throw these weeds on the weed pile."

It took three days for Dad and the boys to get all the weeds out of the garden plot. "This looks great!" exclaimed Dad. "Boys, you can be proud of what you've done."

Steven and Daniel just rolled their eyes. "When can we plant the seeds?" Daniel asked impatiently.

"After two more weedings!"

"Oh, no." Both boys sighed at once.

A week later, Dad was right about more weeds growing. A light green blanket seemed to cover their garden plot. And some of the tough nut grass with its tangle of roots was sending more sprouts to the surface.

Once again, the boys mumbled and grumbled when Dad said, "Let's go weed our garden."

"Do we have to?" whined Daniel. "I'd rather do homework."

"This is homework," Dad replied. "Let's call it summer school!"

"Oh, brother," complained Steven. "I hate *all* homework," he muttered under his breath as he reluctantly picked up a trowel and began digging out the pesky weeds around him.

Three days later, their garden plot was still weed free. At least they couldn't see any little, green weeds growing in the rich, black soil.

But a week later, guess what? The weeds were back. Not so many, but enough to make the boys start thinking up every excuse in the book—and a few more—to try and get out of the weeding.

It wasn't as if the boys had to work in the garden all day—or even every day. Dad sometimes took them with him to different neighborhoods to sell books. They also had plenty of time to play catch, tag, or hide-and-seek. They spent hours gliding on their rope swing. Plus, Dad made sure that they got to their favorite beach for swimming and snorkeling. But, every time he suggested they do a little weeding, the grumbling began.

Dad tried to encourage the boys by rewarding them for a positive attitude, praising them for a job well done, and talking to them about how the soil in the garden is like their hearts and minds. If they planted good seed in the soil, they would get a good harvest, just like if they plant good character traits in their lives, like industriousness, honesty, a good attitude, and responsibility, these will bear fruit and people will appreciate them and respect them for the good work they do. But even the object lessons seemed to go in one ear and out the other. Nothing Dad did seemed to motivate the boys to do their best—at least not with the weeding.

It was getting near the end of the three week weeding period when Dad decided to rope off certain areas of the garden for each boy to weed. Daniel's plot was about fifty feet from Steven's, so they wouldn't be tempted to waste time by playing together. "OK, boys, your job is to pull every weed in your plot. And be sure you get the roots. Do your best because this will probably be the last weeding."

"Hooray!" Steven shouted.

Dad continued, "I have to help the farm owner finish putting on the new roof of a house, so I'm going to leave you to weed your part of the garden. The faster and more efficiently you can work, the sooner you can go play. It's all up to you."

Both boys began with enthusiasm. But soon Steven got hot, tired, and cranky. When he was sure Daniel wasn't looking, he took some weeds that had previously been dug up and added them to his new pile to make it look like he had pulled more weeds. Then, instead of getting the roots out, which took a great deal of effort—especially the nut grass—he just pulled off the top leaves and covered the tangled roots with some soil.

In no time, his plot looked good. "I'm done," he announced, and ran over to play on the rope swing. Daniel had just barely done half of his plot.

When Dad returned, he could tell that Steven had done a sloppy job. He could see weeds hiding under the soil's surface, but he just asked, "Steven, are you sure you weeded properly?"

"Oh yes, Dad."

"Did you pull up all the roots?"

"Sure did, Dad, just look at all the weeds in that pile." As soon as the words were out of Steven's mouth, he felt guilty. But he didn't retract his statement.

"Well then, if you are sure your plot has been weeded correctly, this will be your own special garden to plant."

Steven looked perplexed. He knew he hadn't weeded correctly, and he didn't like the idea that this would be his plot. But he didn't change his story, and he went ahead and planted the seeds his dad gave him.

Three weeks later, Steven's plot was filled with weeds, while the rest of the garden showed a large variety of vegetables growing in the rich, black soil.

At harvest time, both Dad's and Daniel's plots produced yummy tomatoes, corn, squash, cucumbers, eggplant, potatoes, green beans, and a large variety of herbs. It was, indeed, a Garden of Eden.

But, poor Steven. The only thing he harvested from his Garden of Weedin' was two radishes and lots and lots of weeds! ■

Whatever a man sows, that he will also reap.
—Galatians 6:7, NKJV

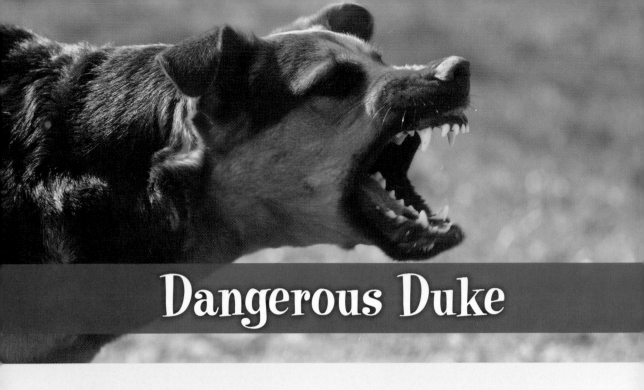

Dangerous Duke

A ngie had a tender heart when it came to animals. She was always bringing home a stray cat or dog to take care of until the owner could be found. Once she even brought home a baby squirrel, caring for him until he grew big enough to scamper away to the great outdoors. However, there was one creature that lived right next door that Angie was absolutely terrified of.

His name was Duke, but most people called him "Dangerous Duke," because of his extremely unfriendly disposition. He belonged to her friend, Lucas, whose family who adopted him from a local animal shelter. They didn't really know what kind of dog he was, but the director at the shelter thought he was a mix of several breeds, although he looked mostly like a Rottweiler. These dogs are known to be very loyal to their family, independent, territorial, and aggressive, and for reasons unknown to his owners, or anyone else, Duke especially hated women, except

for Lucas' disabled mom who he felt was his duty to protect. It might have been due to past abuses, but Duke delighted in barking and chasing females of all ages—including twelve-year-old Angie. Thus far she had managed to stay out of Duke's way by simply being aware of whether or not he was outside. But on a sunny summer afternoon, that all changed.

Photo taken by: Rebekah Blanca

Angie had been enjoying her tree swing when she noticed Lucas was in his yard, jumping on his trampoline. She waved to him and called out, "Hey, Lucas! Can I come over and jump on the trampoline with you?"

Lucas looked at her and grinned, motioning for her to come. "Sure, come on over! I want to show you how high I can go!"

She hopped off the swing and dashed across her yard into his. Soon they were jumping up and down, each trying to see who could go the highest. Suddenly, Angie remembered she hadn't told her mom where she was. "I better ask my mom if I can play in your yard. I'll be right back, OK?"

"Sure," Lucas replied. "I'll practice my special knee-drop trick while you're gone."

Angie climbed down from the trampoline, put her shoes on, and headed toward her house. All of a sudden the back door of Lucas' house opened. His mother stood in the doorway wrestling with something black and brown that she didn't intend to let follow her outside. Angie froze in terror as her eyes locked with Duke's—sending him into such a frenzy that Lucas' mom, try as she might, could not hang on. Breaking free, he bolted down the steps, barking fiercely and running straight toward Angie.

"No, Duke, no!" Lucas' mom screamed. "Come back right now!" But Duke wasn't listening. Instead he barked and growled even louder, determined to reach his target.

In a flash, Angie began running as fast as she could go, back toward her house, hoping to make it to the tree or inside the back door before Duke overtook her. She could hear Lucas and his mother screaming at her. "Stop! Don't run!"

They must be crazy! Angie thought. *The last thing I'm going to do is stop so that beast can have me for lunch!* For her, this was a matter of life and death! Angie's heart was racing faster than she was, and her breath came out in great gasps as Duke gained on her. She could hear his growl getting louder. The sound of his paws thudding after her grew closer. *Just a little farther,* she thought. *Maybe I could climb up my tree swing and get high up into the branches, but no, that might be too risky. What if I can't climb fast enough? And what if a branch breaks? No, my best bet is to run to my back door and get in the house as quick as I can!*

Photo taken by: Rebekah Blanca

Angie was almost in range of the door. She cried out for help, hoping her mom would hear her. *I'm gonna make it! Run a little faster,* she told herself. She ran so fast her glasses fell off her face and landed on the ground, but she didn't even think for a moment of stopping to pick them up!

Angie could feel the dog's hot breath behind her and, with tears streaming down her cheeks, she prepared for one last surge of speed. Gritting her teeth together, she focused her gaze on her destination, picked up her knees higher, pushed off the ground even harder, and felt herself propel forward more swiftly than ever before! She put a few more inches between her and Duke, and her courage strengthened.

Then, without any warning, just when she thought she would surely make it . . . she tripped!

She went down hard, face-first into the dirt, and tumbled. Maybe it was a tree root, or a large rock, or her own tired feet. She didn't know. All she knew was that Duke was upon her in seconds and he wasn't there to play! He came to a sliding stop beside her, and she could feel his loud growl rumbling within his chest. She kicked at him and tried to crawl away—but he was too quick.

She felt his knifelike teeth close around her leg, piercing through her jeans and into her skin. Then he shook her violently. She screamed in pain, wildly kicking at him, desperately trying to get him to release her leg. Instead, his powerful jaws clamped down even harder, and Angie cried out from the searing pain of his teeth puncturing her legs again and again. There was no escaping—she was powerless to stop the dog. She had only one option.

In the midst of this vicious attack where Angie lay helpless, she cried out, "Dear Jesus, please help me! Please help me now!"

Almost immediately, a pack of friendly stray dogs that often ran around the neighborhood came running through her backyard. When Duke saw them, he stopped his attack, watched them for a moment, and then, deciding that his doggie friends looked like more fun than biting Angie, took off after them. Angie watched in amazement as Duke disappeared down the road.

Breathless, Lucas' mother came hobbling over, with Lucas close behind. Dropping her crutches on the ground, she fell to her knees and wrapped her arms around the frightened girl.

"Are you OK?" Lucas' mom cried. "I'm so very sorry. I was just too weak to hold on to Duke." Then she yelled for Angie's mom to come quickly. Hearing no response, she turned to her son, "Lucas! She can't hear me. Quick! Go knock on the door!"

Lucas bounded up the steps, pounded on the door and screamed, "Hurry! Duke bit Angie, and her leg is bleeding!"

Within seconds, Angie's mom appeared. She rushed Angie to the hospital where the doctor treated her bleeding wounds, and a nurse gave her a shot to protect her from rabies.

"Your injuries could have been much worse," the doctor said. "You're a lucky girl."

"No, not lucky," she replied. "I asked Jesus to help me and I know He answered my prayer. There is no doubt in my mind God sent those dogs to save me from dangerous Duke!" ∎

> *The LORD is my helper; I will not fear.*
> *What can man [or animals] do to me?*
> —Hebrews 13:6, NKJV

Bobby's Big Adventure

Bobby lived in a big house on an old prairie homestead out west near the Canadian Rocky Mountains. His father was a traveling salesman, so he was gone a lot.

Bobby knew his family didn't have much money, but that didn't really matter because he had a lot of fun playing with his little brother and sister. They had trees to climb, their own lake to swim in, and barns for all kinds of pets and animals. It was an ideal place for a twelve-year-old kid—except for one thing.

All the other boys who lived on the neighboring farms had their own horses. Bobby had other pets, and his dad had promised him a horse when he got older, but Bobby felt he was ready for a horse now. More than anything in the whole world, Bobby dreamed of having his very own horse and getting it before winter set in when the snow would be too deep to ride.

One morning at breakfast, Bobby

got up his courage and pleaded, "Dad, I really, really want a horse I can ride, like all the other kids have."

He expected his dad to say, "Sorry, but you're still a little young for that kind of responsibility," or "Horses cost a lot of money, son. And who is going to feed the horse and take care of it?"

But instead, after thinking about Bobby's request for a while, Dad looked at his wife and asked, "What about it, Mom?"

Mom said, "A horse is a lot of work . . . and you could get hurt. Guess we ought to think about it."

Dad nodded his head, "Well, son, that's exactly what we'll do. And when I'm home again in a couple weeks, I'll have an answer for you."

Bobby didn't know what to think. At least his dad hadn't said "No." So while Dad was away, Bobby continued to do his chores and whatever Mom asked, all the while dreaming about getting his very own horse.

Two weeks later, a loud honk in the yard told everyone that Dad was home. The kids all wrapped their arms around him and Mom got her hug and kiss. But before Dad even had time to come inside, Bobby asked, "What about my horse?"

Dad just smiled and started talking about other things. Bobby was so curious he could hardly stand it. *What has Dad decided?*

Surely, he thought, *Dad will say something tonight at supper.* But supper came and went, and Dad talked about everything else . . . but horses.

Bobby knew better than to beg, so he waited, even though it was the hardest thing in the world to do!

Bobby worried that his dad may just be putting off bad news. He was afraid his dad didn't think he was old enough yet. By Sunday morning, Bobby had almost given up. He was never going to get his very own horse—at least not this year.

But at breakfast, Dad surprised Bobby by announcing, "Bobby, I think you are ready for your very own horse, and I think I have found just the one!"

"What?" Bobby's eyes grew wide in amazement. He couldn't believe what he was hearing.

"Yes," said Dad, "the only problem is the horse ranch is twenty-eight miles away, and we don't have a horse trailer. You're going to have to ride your horse by yourself all the way home. It will probably take all day, so we'll have to start early tomorrow morning and pray that the weather's good."

After a pause, Dad asked, "Well, Bobby, do you think you're old enough for that kind of responsibility?"

"Oh, yes, Dad. Don't worry about me. I've been riding the neighbor's horses for the past year, and I've only fallen off twice. I'm strong and tough. I can do it."

"I know you can, son, especially if you remember to claim God's promise in Psalm 91:11, 'For He shall give His angels charge over you, to keep you in all your ways.'"

Early the next morning, Dad shook Bobby, "Wake up, cowboy! Dress warm—it's cold out. Think you're ready for your big adventure?"

"Yes, Dad. I've been claiming that promise about the angels taking care of me."

At family worship time, Dad read once again about how God sends angels to protect His children. Everyone prayed that Bobby and his new horse would arrive home safely. Then Bobby grabbed the sack lunch that

Mom had made for him, and they were off.

The twenty-eight-mile ride down the paved road didn't take very long by car. Soon they made a sharp turn over a cattle guard and entered a big horse ranch where they were met by a burly rancher and two shepherd dogs. "Good morning!" the man shouted. "Name's Anderson. You're Bobby, aren't you?" he said, motioning toward Bobby. "I understand you folks are looking for a good saddle horse. Well, you've come to the right place."

Mr. Anderson leaned over the fence and shouted to the dogs, "Bring 'em in." The dogs were gone in a flash.

In a few minutes, a pounding herd of twenty-five or thirty horses came galloping into the barnyard with the dogs nipping at their heels. Satisfied with the morning run and their duty done, the dogs lay down nearby, waiting for their next order.

"I've got the perfect horse for you, kid. She was raised up with my four children, all gone to the big cities now, leaving me and their ma, the dogs, and the horses. This little mare is very gentle, but a little older now. She'll ride, rope, pull a cart or buggy, and will never run away on you."

"Here, Misty," he called, and out of the milling herd came a sorrel mare. She reached over the rail fence and nuzzled the rancher. "She wants oats," he said, reaching for a half-full bucket, in which she happily thrust her nose and came up with a mouth full. Bobby reached over to pet her. She nudged him, slobbering oats down the front of him.

He laughed. "She likes me. We're going to be good friends."

"Take good care of her," said the rancher, "and she will last you for years.

"Now buckaroo," the rancher continued, "you're going to have to ride her home. But I'll tell you what I'm going to do. Since my kids are all gone and I wanted to find a good home for Misty where someone will love her and take care of her, I'll make you a deal. For an extra twenty-five dollars, I'll throw in Misty's saddle, bridle, and halter, along with a half bag of feed for her at noon. How's that for a bargain?"

"Done deal," Dad said.

Bobby saddled Misty up, then put the half sack of oats behind the saddle and the rope on the horn. He mounted, galloped around the yard, and then waved at the old rancher and his dad as he headed down the road toward home. Dad jumped into the car, waved as he passed Bobby, and drove on.

With twenty-eight miles to go, Bobby and Dad had figured that Bobby should trot Misty for a while, then gallop for a while, then bring Misty back to a fast walk—and at that rate they should make it home before dark.

What they didn't bargain on was the two ferocious, barking dogs that came running out on the road. Misty reared up on her hind legs and flung her feet out, threatening the dogs until they backed off.

Then, once again, they charged her. Bobby hung on for dear life. Misty wheeled and let her heels fly. The dogs backed off again. Just then the farmer's wife came out of the house, waving her hands and yelling at the dogs, "Come back here! Come back!" Reluctantly, the dogs backed off. The woman shouted, "Sorry about that. They always bark at strangers!"

Bobby breathed a sigh of relief and urged Misty forward. Meeting furious dogs was scary, but Bobby's worst fear was that they would meet a large herd of cattle that were being moved from one pasture to another. Full grown, these animals weighed a half-ton or more, and they didn't mind pushing or running over you, if you got in their way.

At lunchtime, Bobby stopped at a roadside pond where Misty could get a drink. He pulled down the half sack of oats for Misty, and while she chomped away, he ate his sack lunch. He was starved. Soon it was time to be on their way again.

Clouds gathered overhead and Bobby shivered as the temperature began to drop. Topping a hill, Bobby's worst fears were realized. Coming out of a feeder lot were more than a hundred head of big cattle with three cowboys whooping it up, trying to move the cattle along. With water on both sides of the road, there was no place to go. Misty snorted and stood her ground. Bobby prayed, "Lord, I need an angel. If I get knocked down or Misty gets run over, we're both gone."

Misty braced herself. She didn't like cattle either. She bared her teeth as if to dare them to run over her. Amazingly, the herd divided and went around them. One of the cowboys yelled as he passed, "Good stand, kid, you've got a great horse there."

Bobby thought so too, and thanked God for the angel's protection.

Later in the afternoon, a few large snowflakes drifted down. Just ahead was the Red River Bridge. It looked huge and threatening. Stepping on the bridge, the hollow sound of the planks scared Misty. She stopped and wouldn't budge. Bobby pushed, shoved, dragged, cried, and prayed again, "Dear Lord, I need help. Please help me get Misty across before a big storm breaks."

Suddenly, a red pickup pulled to a stop and Kelly, a horse trader from down the road, asked, "What's wrong?"

"Misty's never seen a bridge like this before and she's scared," Bobby replied.

"Here, I'll help you," was his response. "You've got to think like a horse." Reaching into the back of his pickup, Kelly pulled out a feed bucket half full of oats. "Here, sit on the tailgate and hold this between your knees. Your horse will stick her nose in it and she'll follow us right across."

Safely on the other side, Kelly said, "You're on your own now, kid. In an hour or so you'll be home and everything will be all right."

Soon they trotted through their front gate and Dad and Mom ran out to meet them.

"You made it, son. We're so proud of you," Dad said as he gave Bobby a hug.

Later, stripping off the bridle and saddle, Bobby brushed Misty down and prayed, "Dear Jesus, thank You for Misty and for Your protection on my first big adventure!" ■

> *I will guide you with My eye.*
> —Psalm 32:8, NKJV

Runaway Jumper

When Michael and Jason first saw their new Golden Labrador puppy, the boys knew her name had to be Jumper. After all, when they stooped down to look at all the puppies, the little dog literally jumped into their arms.

Jumper wasn't much of a guard dog, but she was very gentle and very, very friendly. She dearly loved her family, but there was one problem. She was curious. Whenever she got the chance, she would run away.

Dad put her on a line in the backyard so she could get lots of exercise during the day. But no matter what kind of a collar they put around her neck, she would wiggle out of it. When she got loose and was running around exploring, she was so friendly that if a stranger thought she was lost and coaxed her into their car, Jumper would willingly get in. As a result, she sometimes ended up several towns away.

Fortunately, she wore an additional

Grandma and Jason

collar with tags attached. Everyone who picked Jumper up noticed the telephone number and would call. Then Michael, Jason, and their parents would go and bring her back home.

But what if someone didn't call? What if someone decided they wanted to keep Jumper?

One afternoon when Jumper turned up missing, Jason called his grandmother on the phone. "Oh, Gwamma, can you please pray for

Jumper loves all the attention she gets from Michael.

Jumper, NOW?" He was all out of breath. "She ran away again and Dad and Michael are out looking for her. She's been gone a long time, longer than ever before. Oh, Gwamma, can you pray and ask Jesus to bring Jumper home? 'Cuz she's our dog and we want her back!"

Grandma assured Jason that Jesus loved him and that Jesus loved Jumper. "But," she said, "that doesn't mean that Jesus always answers our prayers in just the way we want Him to. What's important, Jason, is that Jesus always hears our prayers and will give us the best answer. Let's pray together right now."

Over the phone Jason heard his grandma pray, "Dear Jesus, You know that Jumper has run away from home and we want to ask You to please watch over her. We don't want anything bad to happen to her. Michael and Jason love her very much. Please, dear Jesus, if it is Your will, let Jumper come home. Thank You, Jesus, for hearing and answering our prayer. In Your precious name I pray. Amen."

Just as Grandma said, "Amen," she heard Jason screaming into the phone. "Gwamma, Jesus answered our prayers already! Jesus answered our prayers!" Grandma heard the front door open and Jumper come bounding into the house with Michael and Dad right behind her! Dancing with excitement, Jason dropped the phone on the floor.

After hearing a lot of commotion in the background as the boys hugged

Jumper, telling her how much they loved her and scolding her for running away, Grandma heard Jason's older brother, Michael, come on the line.

"Hello, is anyone there?" he asked.

"Yes, honey, it's Grandma!"

"Oh, Grandma! You won't believe it, but Jumper ran away again and you know how she is when she runs! She never comes when we call." Michael barely paused to catch his breath. "We looked and looked for her. Dad and I drove all over the neighborhood and just when Dad said we would have to go home and look again tomorrow, I saw her running along the sidewalk. Dad stopped the truck and yelled for her to come. And Grandma, believe it or not, she stopped,

Jason with his mom, Rebecca Lynn.

looked at us, and then ran toward us and hopped into the truck! That has never happened before, Grandma! Can you believe it?"

Grandma chuckled. "Yes, Michael, I can believe it because while you were looking for Jumper, Jason called me and we were asking Jesus to take care of Jumper and let her come home!"

"Well, Jesus sure answered your prayer fast, Grandma."

"He sure did, sweetie."

Michael started giggling. "Stop licking me, Jumper. Here Grandma, Jason wants to say something."

There was a pause until Jason's voice came on the line. "Gwamma?"

"Yes, Jason?"

"Jesus must love Jumper an awful lot, huh, Gwamma?"

"Yes, He does, Jason. And He loves you and Michael even more." ■

Before they call I will answer;
while they are still speaking, I will hear.
—Isaiah 65:24, NIV

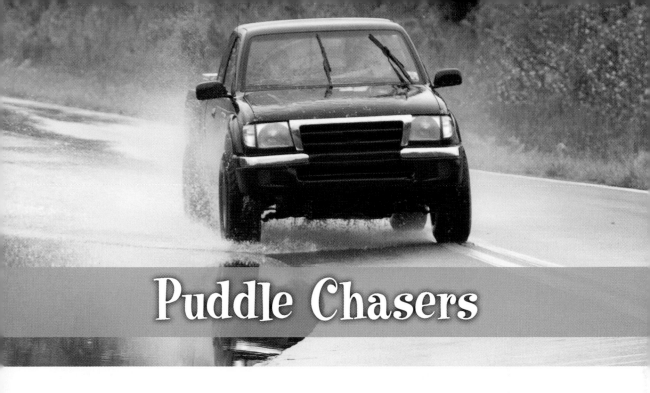

Puddle Chasers

Megan flicked through the channels on the TV one more time. There was nothing on and she was bored, bored, bored. The rain had eased finally, but there was still the melodic trickle of water running off the roof. It had rained for three days straight, right in the middle of the school holidays.

Megan had tried calling three different friends to come over and hang out, but none of them answered the phone. They were probably doing something exciting, unlike her. She could feel a black cloud of disappointment forming in her head. Everyone got to do exciting things but her. During the last vacation, Taylor had gone to Sea World. Megan had to be content with riding the Ferris Wheel at the county fair. Kayla had gone to the water park down by the ocean. Megan swam in her grandparents' tiny pool where the water barely came up to her waist. Brooke had gotten her own laptop. Megan wasn't even allowed to

play on the computer for more than a couple hours a week.

Dad came into the room with a big smile on his face and truck keys in his hand. "Come on, Megan," said Dad. "Let's go have some fun."

"I don't feel like it," grumbled Megan.

Dad tousled her hair. "Got a case of the grumps, have you?" said Dad. "I know just the thing to fix that."

Megan pulled her head away and smoothed down her hair. "I just want to stay here." She flicked through another ten channels with the remote.

Dad sat down next to Megan on the couch and bumped her gently with his shoulder. "The rain's got you down in the dumps, has it?"

Megan could feel Dad staring at her but didn't turn to face him. "Let's go for a drive instead of hanging around here all day," said Dad. "I promise it will be fun."

Megan sighed. There was no point. Dad wouldn't give up until she agreed. "Fine," said Megan, "but don't expect me to enjoy it."

Dad laughed, which made Megan frown even more, and she threw up her hands in mock defeat. "OK, Miss Cranky Pants, I promise not to expect you to enjoy yourself." He wrapped an arm around Megan's shoulder. "But I'm glad you've decided to come with me. You never know what might happen."

Megan slumped into the seat of Dad's black pickup truck, tilted her head back, and closed her eyes. She had no idea where they were going, and she really didn't care. Dad probably had to run to the hardware store and just wanted some company.

They drove in silence for a long time. Megan tried not to care where they were going, but when they'd gone past the grocery store, the hardware store, and the fruit market, three of her dad's favorite places to go, she couldn't hold back her curiosity any longer. "Where are we going?" she asked.

Dad smiled. "I thought you'd never ask. Just let me swing a left here, and at the end of the street we'll hang a right and we'll be there." He glanced over at Megan and grinned. "I think you're going to love this."

Megan felt a bubble of excitement grow in her stomach and she sat up straight in her seat, straining to see around the corner. As her dad rounded the bend, he pulled the truck over to the side of the road and came to a stop. "Look at that," said Dad. "Now doesn't that look like fun?"

Megan stared at the long, black stretch of road in front of her and gave up on trying not to smile. "Dad, that's awesome!" she said. This was no ordinary road. Like a piece of thick, black licorice, it lay straight in front of Megan for as far as she could see, but it was as though someone had grabbed a rope and shook it, making it undulate and wobble like a snake. The road had hill after hill after hill after hill—with no side roads and no traffic. And best of all, in between the hills, right at the lowest point of each section, were puddles.

Megan turned to her dad, eyes wide. "You're not going to do what I think you're going to do, are you?"

"Yep," said Dad, "I certainly am. My dad brought me here after every big rain when I was a kid. And don't worry, the puddles are never more than an inch or two deep, but they sure know how to make a splash." He revved the truck's engine and laughed. "Got your window up, kiddo?"

Megan double-checked her window and grinned. "Yep."

"Ready? Tighten your seatbelt! Let's go chase some puddles!"

Dad took off and let the truck roll down the first hill, gaining speed until it hit the bottom of the dip, right where an enormous, but shallow puddle was spread across the road. A rooster-tail of water sprayed up over the hood and along the side of the truck, drowning Megan's window in rainwater. "Wow!" said Megan. "That was awesome."

They climbed to the top of the next hill and coasted down into another puddle. A wall of water washed over the truck and Megan felt the force of it slow them down. "Quick! The next one!" said Megan.

They drove through puddle after puddle after puddle, until Megan's sides ached from laughing so hard. And when they got to the end of the hills, her dad turned the truck around and came back through the other way. This was more fun than any theme park or bowling alley!

When they crested the final hill for one last time, Dad pulled the truck over to the side of the road so they could both catch their breath.

Megan turned to her dad and grinned. "Thanks, Dad. That was great!"

Dad grinned back. "It was, wasn't it? You know, sweetheart, here's

what I think. When God gave Adam and Eve the Garden of Eden, He could have made it boring and bland, but He didn't. He filled it with interesting things to explore, places to go, and animals to discover. I think God wants us to do the same. And fun doesn't have to cost money, either."

As Dad drove home, Megan thought for a while. Dad was right. Here she'd been feeling sorry for herself and down in the dumps, and a simple drive in the truck with her dad had turned a ho-hum day into something awesome.

"Hey, Dad," said Megan.

"Yes, sweetie?" said Dad.

"Sorry for sulking earlier." Megan could feel her cheeks getting hot at the admission.

"And thanks for the apology," said Dad. "You know you're far better looking with a big smile on your face."

Megan laughed. "Can I call Taylor, Brooke, and Kayla when I get home? I want to tell them how much fun we had today chasing puddles."

Dad smiled and nodded his head. "Sounds like a plan, Megan. Sounds like a great plan indeed." ■

> *Rejoice always.*
> — 1 Thessalonians 5:16, NKJV

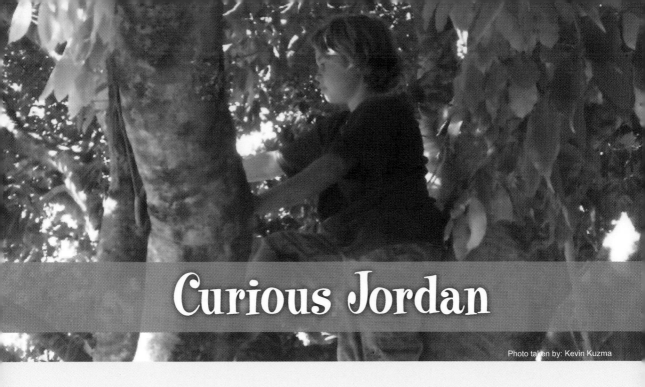

Curious Jordan

Photo taken by: Kevin Kuzma

"Sometimes I hate summer," Jordan muttered to himself as he escaped out the front door. Thankfully, neither his older brother, Conner, or baby sister, Lillian, had seen him. Jordan knew it was his responsibility to help Conner watch Lillian until Mom came home, but it was hard sometimes. Conner thought he was all grown up because he was a teenager now, and he spent most of his time texting his friends or playing video games. That left Jordan stuck changing diapers and entertaining their two-year-old sister.

Jordan desperately looked for somewhere to hide; a place where he could be alone for a while and just think. If he could find a hideout, maybe Conner wouldn't notice he was missing until Mom got home.

Jordan's thoughts turned to his mother. He knew he should be inside washing dishes or doing the laundry. Mom would be tired when she got home; he knew that much. It had been hard for her since the divorce, and now it was even harder since she started having problems with her health.

Jordan silently worried, *What will happen to us if we lose Mom? Who would take care of us?* Wiping a stray tear drop from his eye with the back of his hand, Jordan scanned the yard for a quiet spot. Then his eyes rested on the only tree in the desolate yard. The new, green leaves promised some protection. *Maybe if I climb the tree and stay really still, Conner won't find me,* he thought to himself as he ran to his only option of escape.

Scaling the tree quickly, Jordan buried himself in the leaves and contorted his body to fit one of the branches. Soon his mind began to wander. He imagined he was far away on an island with white, sandy beaches. He began to relax so much that he nearly fell asleep. The sensation of his body beginning to fall jolted him back to reality.

As he repositioned himself and tried to calm his racing heart, he noticed a woman dressed in a business suit walking up the other side of the street. *Can that be Mom?* he wondered. Jordan watched as the woman carried a heavy briefcase to the door of a house. *Oh, she must live over there,* he thought. But then, the woman knocked on the door instead of entering the house! When a lady answered the door, the business woman showed her something from inside her bag. *She must be selling something.* Jordan thought to himself, *Maybe it's candy bars like the ones we have to sell for school.* Jordan felt his stomach growl. *Maybe she'll give me one if she can't sell enough,* he dreamed wistfully.

Eagerly he watched as the woman went to several other houses, but few people were home. He wished he could see what it was that she was trying to sell. Finally, the woman began to walk down the same side of the street as Jordan's house was on. She was only stopping at homes where the cars were in the driveway, so Jordan knew she wouldn't stop at his house. Suddenly, he felt an urgency to know what the woman was selling. Just as she passed by his tree, Jordan shouted, "Hey!"

Photo taken by: Kevin Kuzma

The startled woman turned around in all directions, trying to see where the voice came from.

Jordan laughed as he climbed down the tree. "What are you selling?" he asked boldly.

The woman laughed and smiled as she said, "Would you like to see?"

"Sure!"

But the woman didn't pull chocolate bars out of her bag. Instead, she took out several colorful books. The books had stories about kids making good choices, and others had Bible stories in them. But the one that Jordan wanted to look at the longest was one that had a huge picture of a kind-looking Man in it.

"Would you like me to read you one of the stories in this book?" the woman asked.

When Jordan nodded his head, she sat down on the curb, even in her nice suit, and read to him. Jordan felt a warm fuzzy feeling in his heart as the woman read the story of a Man called Jesus who could solve people's problems and even cared about kids.

Jordan carefully held the book the woman now placed in his hands. "Would you like to buy this book?" the woman asked kindly.

"Oh, I'd really like that, but I know we can't afford it. Besides, my mom isn't home and I'm worried about her," Jordan said, wiping away a pesky tear.

"Did you know that you can talk to Jesus any time you want to? You can tell Him when you're afraid and when you feel alone, and He will love you as much as He loved the children in the story. Do you have a Bible in your house?" the woman asked.

"Yes, we do, but we never read it," Jordan answered shyly.

"Well, you can read it all by yourself! And you can talk to Jesus all by yourself too. Have you ever asked Jesus to be your Savior?" the kind lady asked.

Jordan shook his head no.

"Would you like Jesus to forgive you of all your sins and comfort you when you feel alone?" she asked.

Jordan felt the warm feeling really strong now and his heart began to pound, "I would, but I don't know how," he said.

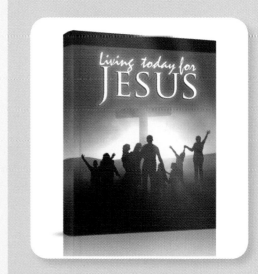

"Well, it's not hard, I'll help you. Is there anything you want to tell Jesus about when we pray?" she asked.

Jordan bowed his head nervously, "I want Him to be with my mom and help her to feel better," he said.

"OK, let's talk to Jesus right now. I'll say some words and you can say them after me. Dear Father in heaven . . ." the woman started.

"Dear Father in heaven . . ." Jordan repeated.

"I know that I have sinned and done bad things. Please forgive me. I believe that You died on the cross to save me and I accept Your gift. Please come into my heart and teach me more about You. And please be with my mom so she won't be sick anymore. In Jesus' name, Amen." The woman prayed, and Jordan repeated each sentence after she said it.

When they opened their eyes, Jordan felt like a huge rock was lifted off of his chest. He felt excited and wished he could keep the Jesus book, but he didn't ask. Instead, he gave it back.

As the woman got up to leave, she handed Jordan the book, "I think Jesus would want you to have this book, so I'd like to give it to you. And don't forget, you can learn more about Jesus in the Bible, and you can pray to Him anytime you want. Just talk to Him like you would a friend. When you mess up, tell Him all about it, and He will forgive you and help you just like He did today." And with that, the woman was gone.

Jordan held the precious book in his hands. He would never forget this day—the day that a simple prayer taught him how to grow close to the best Friend he would ever have.

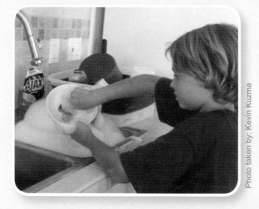

Photo taken by: Kevin Kuzma

Then suddenly, he didn't feel like hiding anymore. Mom would be home soon and he wanted to have those dishes washed and the laundry started. And then, maybe, he would have time to read the Jesus book to Lillian. Summer wasn't so bad after all! ■

If you ask anything in My name, I will do it.
—John 14:14, NKJV

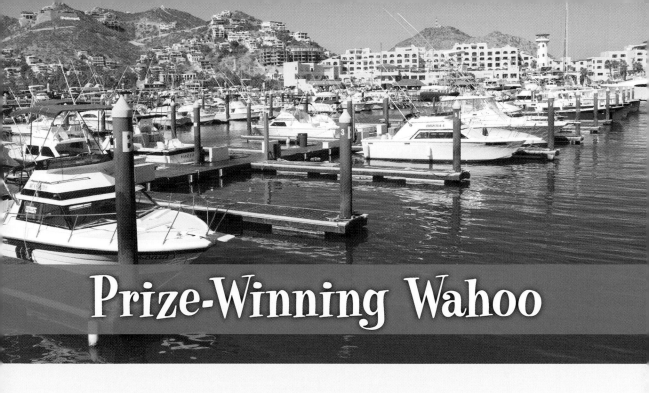

Prize-Winning Wahoo

Rich had been doing odd jobs and saving his allowance for months for a fishing trip in Los Cabos, Mexico. He knew it took a lot of money to rent a boat, but ever since his uncle Don had caught a five-foot Wahoo and everyone *oohed* and *aahed* over the pictures of the big fish, Rich had dreamed of catching a big one just like his uncle.

Rich's family took a vacation down to the tip of Baja California every year. They loved snorkeling at Chilano Bay, sunbathing on Santa Maria Beach, and surfing along East Cape. But most of all, Uncle Don enjoyed renting a Mexican panga fishing boat and heading up along the Pacific Coast in search of Rooster Fish, Yellow Tail, and the prized Wahoo.

Although most of the family were vegetarians and didn't eat fish, Uncle Don loved the challenge of hooking the big ones, the struggle of reeling them in, and finally, the satisfaction of landing them. If the fish was big enough, he would take pictures and then either throw the fish back into the water or give it to a poor, hungry family.

This year, Uncle Don had finally said Rich was old enough to go out fishing with him! This would be the most wonderful fishing trip of his life. He would have his own rod and reel, and he was going to catch the big one.

The night before, Rich helped get everything ready. They made a lunch of peanut butter sandwiches, carrot sticks, and apples. They got suntan lotion, windbreakers, their fishing tackle, and loaded the car. The alarm rang at five in the morning. After a quick breakfast of oatmeal and a big glass of freshly squeezed orange juice, Rich and his uncle quietly closed the door to their condo, jumped in the car, and headed out to the harbor at Cabo San Lucas. Roberto, the captain of the panga, was waiting with fresh bait and all the equipment necessary for a successful day of fishing along the Pacific Coast.

The sky was just beginning to lighten as they headed out of the harbor, past the resorts, around the arch at Land's End, and up along the rugged coastline. *Bump, bump, bumpity, bump, bump,* the hard fiberglass seat that Rich was sitting on pounded against the waves as the motor purred, leaving the lights of the resorts far behind. Rich shivered as the brisk ocean air swept across his face. The windbreaker felt good. In fact, he wished he had taken along a heavier jacket. But in less than an hour, he knew the sun would break above the horizon and its hot rays would be beating down on them. Then off would come his windbreaker.

Roberto, having the job of arranging the trolling rigs, asked Rich if he would like to steer the boat. "Really, you mean it?" Rich asked.

"Just keep it in a straight line up the coast." For a kid who loved the ocean, boats, and fishing, life couldn't get much better. It was a dream come true to pilot a Mexican panga while Roberto went to the back of the boat to tie on the hooks and bait.

The sun was up now. Rich glanced toward the frigate birds floating on the wind currents in the cloudless, blue sky overhead. How effortless they glided, banked, and swooped without ever flapping their gray-tipped black wings.

Suddenly, the panga was surrounded by California Sea Lions. Rich had seen pictures of the big sea lions and had watched them sunbathe on a rock next to the arch, but he had never before seen them swim so close. He was amazed at how big they were. The problem was they were feeding on the same fish that Rich hoped to be catching in a few minutes.

On they went, past long stretches of sand dune beaches and jagged patches of rocks. Just past a new lighthouse that was being built on the point, Rich handed back the piloting of the boat to Roberto, who skillfully kept the panga on the brink of the crashing ten-foot surf while Rich and his uncle kept their eyes on the tips of the four rods, watching to see if a fish would take the bait.

Each time the rod would vibrate and then dip down, one of them would jump up, grab the rod, yank back to set the hook, and then begin to reel the fish in. That's when the fun began—the race to see who would get the fish first—a sea lion or a fisherman.

At one point, Rich had a big one on his line, when the fish jumped in the air, attracting the attention of a sea lion. Rich wound in the line as fast as he could. Roberto grabbed the line to help but, alas, the sea lion was faster. It swallowed the fish, then turned around and started pulling the panga in the opposite direction—until the line broke. Then the sea lion expertly spit out the head of the fish, along with the lure. It was quite a performance.

After a couple hours of catching nothing but a couple small Sierras, which the captain said he'd use for bait, they decided to try some bottom fishing around the jagged rocks, so they headed to a sea mount—which is a pile of rocks where fish like to hide. That's when they noticed an eighteen-foot aluminum boat anchored close to the rocks that appeared to be having engine trouble. Roberto steered close enough to yell to the three young men who were frantically working on the motor, "Having trouble?"

"We're dead in the water!" the crew yelled back, making a cut-throat

sign with their hands. "Can you pull us in?"

Roberto turned to Uncle Don. "What do you want to do, keep fishing or help these people? You've hired me to take you fishing. It's your call."

Uncle Don then turned to Rich. "I'll let you decide. This is your special fishing trip. You haven't yet caught the big one that you wanted. If we help them, we won't have time to do any more fishing."

Rich thought about it, looked once more at the people anchored near the rocks, and said, "I think we should help them."

A few minutes later, the fishing lines on the panga were pulled in, the anchor on the aluminum boat was pulled up, the anchor rope was tied on to the panga, and the little fishing boat began moving away from the rocks toward the harbor.

As Rich looked back at the boat they were towing, he thought, *What would Jesus have done?* He remembered the stories of how Jesus told the fishermen to cast out their nets on the other side of the boat—and then Jesus filled their nets with so many fish the nets nearly broke. He thought about how Jesus calmed the storm and saved the disciples in the fishing boat from drowning. And he thought about Jesus feeding fish to all the hungry. Not once did Jesus try to go after a fish for Himself. Rich smiled as he thought, *Just like the disciples, I started out fishing for fish—and ended up fishing for men, while the prize-winning Wahoo got away.* ■

> *Jesus . . . went about doing good . . .*
> *for God was with Him.*
> —Acts 10:38, NKJV

Bad Bad Blackie

No one knew why Bad Bad Blackie came to town. No one knew where Bad Bad Blackie came from. But everyone remembered the day Bad Bad Blackie arrived—especially Miss Martha.

Miss Martha was the neighborhood cat lady. She kept twelve cats fed and happy in her backyard. Whenever the neighborhood children wanted to hold and pet some kittens, they would go to Miss Martha's yard where there was always one or two basking in the sun. The children also liked to visit Miss Martha at feeding time.

Once in the morning and once at night, Miss Martha would feed her cats. Each cat in the family had its own dish. And each dish had its own spot in the backyard. Fluffy, a big white lap cat's dish was beside the back screen door. Boots, a black cat with four white feet, liked his bowl to be placed on the ground beside the porch. Mi-Mi, a timid Siamese cat, waited by the tool shed for her food. A big, yellow

and white striped cat named Calvin would follow Miss Martha around the yard as she fed each of the other cats until she stopped at his special spot beneath the rambling rose bushes.

On the day Bad Bad Blackie came to town, everything changed for Miss Martha and her twelve cats. Miss Martha grabbed her canvas bag filled with cat food and stepped out of her back door onto her porch, expecting to see her twelve babies lined up and ready to eat. Instead, a giant, black tomcat sat directly in front of the door.

"Well, well, who do we have here? Is your name Blackie?" She leaned down to pet the new arrival. As Miss Martha's hand drew close, the cat growled, hissed, and took a swipe at Miss Martha's hand. The cat's sharp nails left red marks like railroad tracks in her hand. "Ouch! You're not very friendly are you, Blackie? If you're going to act like that I'm going to call you Bad Bad Blackie!"

Calvin, who was cowering beneath the porch, stuck his head out from under the stairs. Bad Bad Blackie whirled about and growled. "It's all right, Calvin. Blackie just doesn't know our way of doing things yet."

Miss Martha glanced around the yard for her other cats. None were in sight. "Fluffy? Fluffy?" she called. From beneath the porch she heard a timid meow.

"Bad Bad Blackie, did you scare away all of my babies?"

Miss Martha filled Calvin's bowl with cat food. "Don't worry, I have enough food for all of you, I promise." She had barely straightened up when Bad Bad Blackie dived into the food.

"Oh, you poor kitty. You must be terribly hungry." Miss Martha resisted the urge to pat Bad Bad Blackie on the head while he was eating.

"Don't worry, Calvin, I'll fill another bowl for you." She walked down the steps and filled Boots' bowl. Before she could fill the next cat's bowl,

Bad Bad Blackie dashed down the steps and began gobbling Boots' food. "Wow, Blackie, you must be really, really hungry."

As Miss Martha filled each bowl around the yard, Bad Bad Blackie gobbled up the food. Whenever one of the cats would challenge the stranger's right to its food, it would be attacked by Bad Bad Blackie and get a swipe across the face.

Day after day, Bad Bad Blackie's feisty behavior continued. Even when Bad Bad Blackie's stomach looked like it might burst if he ate one more mouthful, he claimed every bowl in the yard as his. And all the scolding Miss Martha would do didn't improve his bad behavior one bit.

Bad Bad Blackie didn't stop bullying the other cats when the sun went down. All night long Miss Martha could hear the cats meowing and scrapping outside her bedroom window. A large piece of fur was missing from Fluffy's left ear. Calvin refused to come out from under the porch. Mi-Mi cowered and shook the instant Bad Bad Blackie marched into the yard. Poor Boots tried to stand up to the bully cat, but a swipe across Boots' eye sent him and Miss Martha to the veterinarian for stitches. Even the neighbors began complaining about the big, black cat that was eating all their cats' food.

Miss Martha tried to tame Bad Bad Blackie with love. She always spoke to him in a kind, gentle voice. She would sit and talk with him on her back stoop, trying to lure him closer with kitty treats. But Bad Bad Blackie, though curious, would snarl, scratch, and leap out of reach whenever she tried to touch him. The cat would even threaten the younger neighborhood children playing in their own yards.

It was Friday, the fifth day after Bad Bad Blackie arrived, that Miss Martha and her neighbors agreed that Bad Bad Blackie's reign of terror had to end.

"There's no doubt about it," Mr. Anders demanded, "we need to take Bad Bad Blackie to the animal pound."

Miss Martha groaned. As much trouble as Bad Bad Blackie had been, she didn't want him to be taken to the pound. "Who's going to catch him?" she asked. "I've tried to pet him and I can't get close enough to touch him, let alone catch him in my arms."

"We'll ask the people at the pound to come out and catch him," Mrs. Anders suggested.

The neighbors all agreed it was a great idea.

"It's too late to call the pound today. I'll call the pound on Monday," Miss Martha promised.

And that's when a remarkable event happened in the lives of Bad Bad Blackie, Miss Martha, and her twelve cats.

On Monday morning, Miss Martha cautiously stepped out of her house and onto her porch, expecting to face a snarling, growling Bad Bad Blackie. The screen door had barely closed behind her when the usual bad tempered cat bounded up the porch steps, rubbed against her legs, and purred. Startled, Miss Martha took a step backwards, thinking Bad Bad Blackie would dig his nails into her legs. Instead, Bad Bad Blackie continued to rub against her. Then, when she filled Calvin's bowl with food, Bad Bad Blackie just sniffed Calvin's food, but he didn't touch it.

The cat followed Miss Martha to the next feeding station, and the next, and the next, never eating a morsel of cat food from the other cats' dishes and never spitting or scratching as her twelve cats creeped out of hiding to eat their morning meals.

At the end of the porch, Miss Martha picked up an abandoned pie tin and filled it with food. "Here, Bad Bad Blackie, here's your food." The cat purred and rubbed as if to say thank you. Slowly, timidly, Miss Martha patted Blackie's head as he began eating.

"Whatever happened to you, little guy? How in the world did you change?" Miss Martha sat down on the edge of the porch and watched as Bad Bad Blackie ate his food, never bothering the other cats as they ate theirs. When Bad Bad Blackie finished eating his breakfast, he climbed into Miss Martha's lap and let her pet him for more than fifteen minutes before he sauntered away.

Later in the day, Mr. Anders called. "Have you seen Bad Bad Blackie?" the man asked. "What did you do to him? He's not the same cat."

"I know. I am as surprised as you are! But I didn't do anything to him. When I went out to feed the cats this morning, that's just the way he was," Miss Martha explained.

When the neighborhood children learned about the big difference in Bad Bad Blackie, they came to Miss Martha's backyard to see the cat that changed his attitude. Before, Bad Bad Blackie would hiss, spit, and scratch when any of the children tried to get too close, but now he would run and play with them on the grass. He even allowed eight-year-old Jenny, who lived next door, to dress him in her doll clothes.

No one ever knew what caused Bad Bad Blackie to change, but change he did. Bad Bad Blackie became the nicest, sweetest cat of all. Miss Martha and the children of the neighborhood decided to change Bad Bad Blackie's name to "Beautiful Blackie," to match his change of heart. And from that day on, no one ever saw Bad Bad Blackie again.

Beautiful Blackie

Miss Martha had never before seen a feisty cat like Bad Bad Blackie become gentle overnight, but she has seen lots of people change that fast. God can change the hearts of grumpy girls and bullying boys from bad to beautiful. All they have to do is ask Jesus to come into their hearts. ■

> *Create in me a clean heart, O God;*
> *and renew a right spirit within me.*
> —Psalm 51:10, KJV

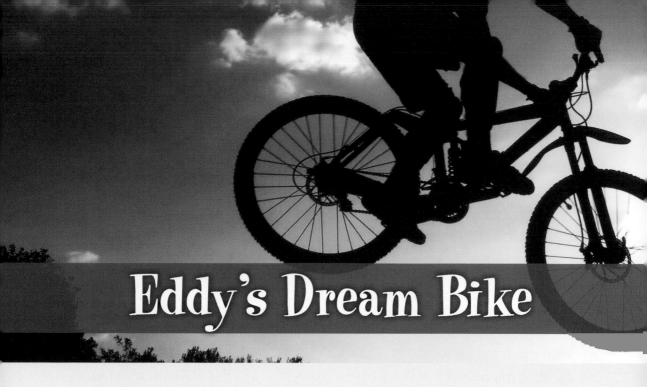

Eddy's Dream Bike

"**C**ome on, Rusty, let's go eat," Eddy called to his German Shepherd as a blast of bitter cold wind blew the barn door out of his hands. Before heading inside, Eddy stopped to glance at the thermometer. Twenty degrees below freezing. *No wonder I'm shivering!* he thought.

Winter had come early to the little farm nestled in the foothills of the Cascade Mountains, bringing with it frigid temperatures and a hefty layer of snow. Money was scarce. With Dad working in town at the lumber mill during the week, the farm chores had fallen into Eddy's hands. It was a big responsibility for a thirteen-year-old.

Eddy stomped the snow from his boots and bounded into the kitchen. The storm door slammed shut behind him. *Yummm!* The aroma of his favorite vegetarian chicken noodle soup and freshly baked corn bread made his mouth water.

"*Brrrr!* It's freezing out there. I can only imagine how cold it will be by morning!"

"There's snow in those clouds too." Mom poured a ladle of soup into a bowl and put it on the table.

Following grace, Eddy buttered a big piece of corn bread and said, "Mom, I've been thinking. I could sure use a new bike this summer." He took a big bite and continued, "I know money's short. I can do odd jobs for the neighbors now, but I could earn a lot more if I had a bike to get me across town."

"Perhaps your father can help you repair your old bike when he comes home," Mom suggested.

"Mom, that bike's hopeless. The frame and both wheels are bent. But I saw a red bike at Henderson's Hardware when I was in town the other day. It's a mighty fine bike—sturdy too." Eddy savored another spoonful of hot soup.

"Eddy," Mom gazed sadly at her son, "I wish we could get you a new bike, but there's no way we can afford it."

Eddy swallowed hard.

"But that doesn't mean God can't give you ideas about how you could earn the money for it," she added.

That night Eddy prayed, "Dear Jesus, please help me think of a way I can earn enough money to get the red bike."

The next day as Eddy finished his morning chores, an idea popped into his head. "Mom! Mom!" he yelled as he rushed into the kitchen, "I've got it! I've got it!"

"Got what?" his mom asked.

"God gave me an idea of how I can earn enough money for the bike."

"How?"

Eddy could barely contain his excitement. "We have seventeen hens and two roosters. As soon as the hens start laying in the spring, I can put a dozen eggs underneath six sitting hens and they'll hatch into seventy-two chicks. I could raise the chicks and then sell them when they are pullets!" (Pullets are "teenage" chickens.)

Mom frowned. "Honey, it sounds good, but lots of bad things could happen. That's why they say, 'Don't count your chickens before they hatch!' "

"I know, I know. But it's worth a try."

"Yes, of course." Mom smiled. "God gave me an idea too. Maybe I could bake some rhubarb pies and sell them. It would bring in some extra money, but that would mean you'd have to do without dessert for a time."

"I don't mind, Mom. A new bike would be worth it."

And so Mom started baking, and Eddy started taking extra good care of the chickens.

The days grew warmer. Soon the hens would start laying.

One day, Eddy decided it was a perfect time to clean out the hen house. He grabbed a broom and scoop shovel, opened the hen house door, and shooed the chickens out into the yard. He had just begun sweeping when he heard a terrible commotion. The hens and roosters were squawking, flapping their wings, and scattering for cover. There in the middle of the yard were the neighbor's four Irish Wolfhounds, each with a Rhode Island Red in his mouth.

"Hey! Get away from my chickens!" he screamed as he began swinging his broom at the dogs. Startled, the wolfhounds bounded out of the yard and vanished over the nearest hill with four of his precious chickens.

After the whirlwind of dust and feathers settled, tears filled Eddy's eyes. His shoulders sagged. With only thirteen laying hens, it would be a struggle to get enough eggs to be able to give each of the six sitting hens a dozen eggs to hatch. Eddy did the only thing he could think of to do. He prayed, "Dear Jesus, help me to work harder so my dream can come true."

But that wasn't the end of his troubles.

The hens started laying and Eddy began putting eggs under the sitting hens. At last he had six mother hens all sitting on a clutch of twelve eggs—just as he had planned. Now he began to count the days. Nineteen, twenty, twenty-one . . . and the eggs began to hatch. That's when disaster struck again.

Eddy and Rusty were doing the farm chores when he heard squawking from the hen yard. This time, a neighbor's dog had a mother hen clamped in its jaws. Rusty charged, growling and bearing his teeth. Fur flew as Rusty attacked the invader. In dogfights, the dog on home territory usually wins. The neighbor's dog knew he was out of his territory, so he dropped the dying hen and fled.

Mom burst through the kitchen door. "Oh, Eddy, I heard the ruckus and came as fast as I could."

His face distorted with grief, Eddy stared down at the dying hen and then at his mother. "What am I going to do with a dozen baby chickens that no longer have a mother to keep them warm?"

Mom walked toward the hen house. "Which chicks are motherless?"

Eddy shrugged. "I don't know. They all look the same to me."

Mom laughed. "What if we gather up the motherless chicks after dark and slip a couple of them under each mother hen? Maybe the hens can't tell the difference either."

It worked. The chicks thrived as summer rolled around. Word got out about Eddy's project. People began placing orders for the growing chickens. It wouldn't be long now until they were pullets and Eddy could begin delivering the chickens to their new homes.

Whenever Eddy went into town he stopped at the hardware store to admire the shiny, red bike in the window. With the money Mom was

making by selling her delicious rhubarb pies and the money he would make from selling his chickens, he would soon have enough for his dream bike.

That's when disaster struck for the third time. Eddy was just heading home from doing some chores for a neighbor, when a threatening, black thundercloud rolled across the sky. Seemingly out of nowhere, hurricane force winds hurled sheets of cold rain and hail at Eddy, forcing him to take shelter beneath a clump of sturdy oak trees beside the road. Huddled under the leaves of the largest oak, Eddy remembered that

he had left his chickens out in the yard. *Surely the storm will kill them,* he thought. He could feel the money for his precious bike slipping through his fingers. "Oh, dear Jesus," he prayed, "please save my chickens."

The storm lifted as quickly as it had come. As soon as the sun burst through the remaining clouds, Eddy ran straight home. In the chicken yard, he found piles of small chickens jammed into fence corners, underneath several inches of hail. Eddy stood in the middle of the hen yard and surveyed the scattered remnants of his dream. All that work and no new bike after all!

With the toe of his boot, Eddy nudged a pile of feathers and melting hailstones. Suddenly, the pile of wet bodies moved. Desperately, he pawed through what he thought was a pile of dead chickens to find that some of them weren't dead after all. Some of the pullets began to wiggle, shake their feathers, and run around the yard, drying out in the warmth of the sun. Fifty-one had survived. He had just enough to supply all his customers. Between the chicken sales and the pie sales, Eddy had enough cash to pay for the chicken feed and to buy the beautiful red bike in the window of Henderson's Hardware Store.

His feet nearly flew down the dirt road toward town. "Mr. Henderson, I know it's not in the window, but I've come for my new bike," he announced.

Mr. Henderson shook his head sadly. "I know how much you wanted that red bike, but yesterday a boy came in and bought it right out of the window."

"No!" Eddy's face fell. He couldn't believe it. He'd missed purchasing his dream bike by one day!

Eddy could see that Mr. Henderson felt terrible too. "I would have saved it for you if I'd known you were so close to purchasing it."

With a twinkle in his eye and a slight grin on his face, Mr. Henderson added, "Yesterday a new bike came in. It's exactly the same as the one you wanted, except it's blue and has a few extra features. Do you want it?"

Eddy's eyes blinked in surprise. "Want it? You bet I want it!" exclaimed Eddy.

The miles flew by as Eddy pedaled his new bike home. He waved and shouted as he entered the yard where Mom and Rusty came running to meet him. "Look, Mom!

My new bike! Mr. Henderson sold the red one yesterday, but he had an even fancier one for the same price!"

Eddy pointed out all the extra features on the blue bike. "Jesus not only helped me save enough money for it—thanks to your help, Mom— but He found me an even better one than I'd dreamed of." ■

> *Delight yourself in the LORD and he will give you the desires of your heart.*
> —Psalm 37:4, NIV

Froggie Throat

Joshua could hardly believe it. Miss Brenda had asked him to sing for *Kids' Time*, the TV show on 3ABN (Three Angels Broadcasting Network) that encourages young people to use their talents to witness for Jesus. Everyone told Joshua that he had a talent for singing. He had sung solos in church, for school programs, at family parties, and for special occasions in his community. But this time, he would sing LIVE for millions of people all around the world—more people than he could ever count! It was quite an honor for a ten-year-old, and he wanted to do his very best.

Joshua had been practicing an hour a day for weeks now. He'd sung the songs so often he could almost sing them in his sleep. Joshua was so confident he knew all the words that he wasn't nervous at all. And then it happened!

"Mom," Joshua croaked as he got out of bed one morning. "I don't feel so good. My head hurts. My throat is scratchy."

Joshua singing for Kids' Time in Knoxville, Tennessee.

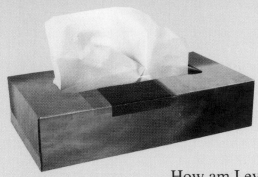

Mom set aside the grapefruit she was peeling, dried her hands on a dish towel, and felt Joshua's head. *"Hmm, you might have a slight fever."*

"A-a-a-choo! A-a-a-choo! This can't be happening. I can't get sick now," Joshua wailed. "It's not fair! How am I ever going to be able to sing?"

Mom gave him a hug and kissed his forehead. "Let's not jump to conclusions, son. It's a full week before you sing in Knoxville."

All week long Joshua did everything he could to avoid coming down with a cold. He ate the right foods, didn't eat sweets, drank plenty of water, and made sure that he got enough sleep every night. Yet no matter how often he told himself, *You can't get sick! You can't get sick!* the message wasn't getting through to his throat. Not only did his head feel clogged, but he sounded like a frog as well.

"Mom, I really don't think I can do this," Joshua complained as they pulled into the Knoxville church parking lot for the rehearsal. He rubbed his throat with his hand. "I just don't think I can sing. Just listen to me. I sound terrible!"

"We're already here, Joshua," Mom said. "You might as well try."

Rehearsal didn't go well at all. Joshua tried to squeak out the notes, but his voice sounded horrible. He came off stage and was so embarrassed that he wanted to run away and hide. He was angry and frustrated. "Why did I have to catch this cold now?" he complained.

His mother tried to encourage him, but when he went to bed that night, doubts swept through his brain with hurricane force.

When Joshua woke up the next morning, he tried to speak and then he tried to sing a few notes, but nothing came out that sounded anything like a melody. Talk about discouraging!

"Mom, I sound like an injured bullfrog! What am I going to do?"

"Let's go find Miss Brenda. Since she's a nurse, maybe she knows something we can do to clear your throat." They climbed into the family car and drove to the church where they found Miss Brenda preparing for the show's taping. She was busy getting everyone else ready, but seeing how distressed Joshua was, she quickly gave him her full attention. Tears glistened in Joshua's eyes as he explained his problem.

Miss Brenda smiled kindly. She could see how frustrated Joshua was. "You know we serve a God of miracles. Why don't we pray about it?"

Joshua and his mother closed their eyes while Miss Brenda prayed. "Dear heavenly Father, You know how disappointed Joshua is that he can't sing his best today. We know that You are the greatest Doctor of all and have the power to heal Joshua's throat. Thank You, Jesus, for what we know You are about to do. We love and trust You in all things. In Your precious name we pray. Amen."

After the prayer, Miss Brenda gently touched his arm. "Remember, Joshua, no problem is too big for God." She gave him a gentle hug and then quickly disappeared to get ready for the program.

At that moment, Joshua wasn't sure how much faith he had. When he went down to practice with his pianist, Wen-Ting Ong, he hoped that her incredible talent on the piano could fill in for his voice and make him sound good. Yet, try as he might, his voice didn't improve.

The excitement in the church grew as other musicians prepared to perform. Joshua kept checking his throat, swallowing hard, trying to get rid of the gunk plastered on his vocal chords.

"Mom, what if I get out there, open my mouth, and nothing but a croak comes out?"

"Honey, either you believe God can heal you or you don't. This is when you have to just trust Him and have faith." His mother patted his

Joshua with Miss Brenda on the new Kids' Time set.

hand to reassure him.

All too soon Miss Brenda took her place on the platform and the show's floor director, Larry McLucas, began counting, "We're going LIVE in five, four, three, two . . ."

Miss Brenda faced the camera and smiled. Joshua heard her say, "Good morning, boys and girls." Everything else she said was a blur. Backstage, Joshua tried to clear his throat and to silence the pounding of his heart. And then he heard Miss Brenda call his name.

"Please be with me, Jesus," Joshua prayed as he stepped to the microphone and cleared his throat one last time. Wen-Ting played the song's introduction. Taking a deep breath, Joshua opened his mouth and the words and music came out of his throat, crisp and clear—better than he had ever sounded before. Joshua could hardly believe it. Was this beautiful sounding melody really coming from his mouth? As he sang the last note, Joshua prayed, *Thank You, Jesus. You are a God of miracles.* ■

> *And my God will meet all your needs according to his glorious riches in Christ Jesus.*
> —Philippians 4:19, NIV

Amazing Web-Spinning Spider

Jasmine was excited to be going on a weekend backpacking trip in the Smoky Mountains of North Carolina with her friends. Since her family had to attend some important meetings in Atlanta, she and her parents were getting a late start. They had told the group leaders to go ahead without them, and as soon as the meetings were over, they would catch up.

"When are we leaving?" Jasmine asked impatiently as she sat on her hotel bed. It was already afternoon. She glanced at her watch. "Mom, it's a long way. It will take us three hours to just get to the state line—and maybe more if there's traffic. And then who knows how long it will take to find the Slide Rock Trail."

"Well, honey, we'll just do the best we can."

Mom and Jasmine were just finishing packing the sack lunch when Dad came rushing into the room. "Hey, gang! Ready to go backpacking? Let's

get out of here."

"Finally," sighed Jasmine as she grabbed her overnight bag and started toward the car.

Within minutes, they were heading toward I-75. The only problem was that it seemed everyone else was leaving Atlanta at the same time. The traffic was stop and go.

Jasmine sighed. She leaned back and shut her eyes, hoping the time would pass more quickly. When she awoke, Dad was driving faster, but they weren't nearly as close to the mountains as they should be. She sighed once more. Mom looked over her shoulder and smiled at Jasmine sitting in the back seat.

"How much farther?" Jasmine asked.

"About seventy-five miles."

"Do you think we'll get there before dark?" Jasmine asked.

"I think we'll get to the trailhead before dark. I just hope the hiking trail is well marked. They said it's about an hour hike in."

Soon the mountains loomed ahead and the roads got steeper and curvier. Mom was reading directions to Dad. "I think you passed it, honey," she said.

Dad pulled off the road, checked the map Mom was holding, then turned around. Jasmine sighed again. This was taking much too long and the sun was going down!

"We're on the wrong side of the river. I think you need to be over there." Mom pointed across the water to another road. Again, Dad turned the car around. Jasmine fidgeted in the back seat.

"Almost there!" Dad said as he made the last turn indicated on the map. By now the sun had gone down behind a mountain range and the sky glowed with a glorious sunset.

Dad parked the car alongside the other cars. Jasmine recognized the van from church, "Yea!" she shouted. "We're here!" Everyone got out of the car and quickly put on their backpacks.

"Get out your flashlights," said Dad. "It will be dark before we arrive at the camp and we've never been on this trail before."

The trio started walking along a well-traveled path. Soon the trail narrowed and, in the deepening shadows, the path became more difficult to see. Dad turned on his flashlight so Mom could see the directions they were supposed to follow. Soon, it was completely dark. They couldn't even see the trail in front of them, except where their flashlights shown. Jasmine began to get nervous.

Mom consulted the directions again. "At the river, turn upstream and follow the trail."

"Hmmm," she paused to look around, shining the flashlight this way and that. "Is this the river?"

"It looks more like a small creek instead of a river," Dad commented as he and Mom searched both sides of the creek looking for a trail. Nothing!

"What do you think we should do?" Jasmine asked.

"Let's keep going," suggested Dad, "Maybe we'll come to a bigger river and we'll find the right trail."

They walked in single file on a very narrow path. The steep mountain wall rose up on the left of the trail. Sometimes the trail narrowed so much their backpacks rubbed against the wall. On their right, they could see the drop-off at the edge of the trail, but how steep it was and what was below, no one knew.

Suddenly, Mom stepped too close to the edge and the dirt under her feet started to give way. One foot slipped and dangled in the emptiness below. She grabbed for something to hang on to, and in that split second, Dad caught her hand.

"You OK?" he asked.

"Yeah," she panted. "I wonder how far that goes down?"

"Let's not find out," Dad said. "I think we need to go back to the creek and look again for another trail. The directions never mentioned that the trail was steep and narrow."

Slowly, the three hikers turned around and walked about twenty minutes back to the creek. Again Dad searched along the sides of the water for a trail, but found nothing.

"Let's pray," said Jasmine.

They bowed their heads while Jasmine prayed, asking for God's protection,

telling Him they were lost and didn't know whether to push on or go back to the car. "Please tell us what You want us to do," pleaded Jasmine. "Amen."

Dad took a deep breath and started once more up the trail they had just been on. Jasmine followed close behind, while Mom brought up the rear. Hopefully, the river and right trail were up ahead.

Suddenly, Dad stopped so quickly that Jasmine ran into him, and Mom ran into Jasmine. "What's going on?" Mom asked.

"Look!" said Dad. He pointed his flashlight in front of him. "I'm sure this wasn't here before." Suspended between two trees and blocking the trail was a huge spiderweb. Sitting in the center was a spider that was as big as the palm of his hand. Everyone took a few steps backward. "Wow, I've seen lots of spiders, but I've never in my life seen one this big!" Dad exclaimed.

Jasmine spoke first. "I think this is God's answer." Without any argument, they turned around and headed back to the car to spend the night.

When the sun began to rise, Jasmine and her parents got up, grabbed their backpacks, and started again on the well-traveled trail that narrowed drastically as it went up the mountain. It seemed much more cheery and safe than it had the night before.

Within minutes, Mr. Jeff, who had arranged the backpacking trip, came walking toward them. "Hi!" he said. "We thought you guys wouldn't make it in the dark, so I got up early to come and show you the way."

As the group continued on the trail, Jasmine asked him, "Did you see the spiderweb that was blocking the trail?"

Mr. Jeff shook his head, "No. Never saw it."

"Spiders can't build a web that quickly and then take it down, can they?" asked Mom. She looked at Jasmine, who shook her head. They walked on quietly.

"Look, Mom!" said Jasmine. "Here is where your foot slid off the trail last night."

Everyone stopped and looked at the steep mountainside that Mom had nearly fallen down. Mom gasped. Had she slipped any farther, she would have fallen a long way down. "Praise God that I caught you in time," said Dad.

As the trail got closer to a much larger stream than they had seen the night before, the roar of the water got louder. Soon there was no visible trail, only boulders to climb up and slide down. When they finally came to the rushing water, Mr. Jeff turned and climbed over the rocks, following the water upstream.

As Dad jumped from rock to rock, he commented, "We would never have been able to do this in the dark. I'm so glad Jesus stopped us on the trail with a giant spider that could spin a web in the dark, and then when the trail was safe, remove it. Pretty impressive, wouldn't you say?"

Jasmine nodded and quietly said, "Thank You, Jesus." ∎

In all your ways acknowledge Him,
and He shall direct your paths.
—Proverbs 3:6, NKJV

The Bear Scare

From the time Noah was a little kid, he was afraid of bears. Not just a little afraid, but really, really, really afraid of bears. He saw bears in shadows, next to rocks, and behind cars. He heard bears in night noises, bumping sounds, and even in the wind.

It didn't help that there was a neighborhood bear that sometimes got into his grandparents' trash. He frequently knocked over their garbage can and rummaged around for leftover goodies. Then, each autumn, in the middle of the night, a bear would steal the apples from their apple tree. He had seen that bear five times in his life; always from the safety of his grandma and grandpa's second-story window. But even then, that was much too close for comfort. There was no way Noah would ever take a chance running into a bear. In fact, sometimes he was so scared of bears that he would dash like a rocket from the door of his grandparents' house to the car, which was only about ten feet away, even

though there was no sign that a bear was anywhere around.

The rest of the family wasn't too concerned about bears, and that bothered Noah. So he was always warning them. "Dad, look! There's a bear." At first, Dad would look and say, "Noah, your imagination is running away with you again. It's just an old rug flapping in the wind that someone hung on a clothesline," or "It's just a bicycle leaning up against the tree." Noah cried *Bear!* so often that Dad wouldn't even look up when Noah shouted.

It was a gorgeous, spring day when the family decided to have a picnic in southern California's San Bernadino Mountains. "Kids, how would you like to go up to Forest Falls and play in the stream?" Mom called to Noah, Jonah, and Hannah. "Dad's going to town for some bread and that special kind of peanut butter with stripes of jelly already in it, so it will be easy to make our sandwiches right up there by the stream. Don't forget your bathing suits."

Photo taken by: Tim Pierce

"Can we take our new buckets and shovels?" Hannah asked.

"Of course. There's plenty of sand in the stream bed to build sand castles with. And Jonah, why don't you grab a ball so we can have a game of catch," Mom added.

The drive didn't take that long and soon they saw the sign for Forest Falls. "Hey, there's a stream over there!" Hannah exclaimed, pointing towards the water.

"This is going to be the best picnic ever," Noah said as Dad drove the car off the main road and parked as close to the stream as possible. "I can hardly wait for lunch!"

"It's going to be a while before we eat," Mom commented. "Why don't you kids explore the waterfall with Dad while I get the blanket out and set up the picnic."

Dad and the kids headed upstream, jumping from rock to rock. The roar of the waterfall got louder and louder. There was just enough water to get wet, but not enough to go swimming in. Besides, the water was freezing cold.

After exploring the base of the waterfall, the boys started throwing rocks and skipping them in the steam. Soon that grew old and they started splashing each other. Hannah screamed in protest, "Don't get my hair wet!" When Dad reminded the boys to respect their sister's wishes—with the kind of look that said, "You better obey," it took all the fun out of their water fight.

"What about building a dam?" Dad suggested as he began moving around some of the larger rocks in the stream bed, causing the water to cascade over the top and making a slightly deeper pool on the uphill side.

Photo taken by: Tim Pierce

Hannah loved the feel of the sand and pebbles under her feet. "It's like walking in a fish aquarium!" she exclaimed.

"I wonder if there are any fish in this stream?" Jonah said.

With the mention of fish, Noah thought about bears and looked around. "I wonder if there are any bears in these woods?"

"Oh, you and your bears!" Jonah teased. "Even if there were bears, they wouldn't be next to this little old steam, because if there are any fish in here, they would be so small that the bears couldn't even see them."

"Smile," Dad called as he aimed his cell phone camera at the kids. They stopped digging in the sand for a minute, smiled at the camera, and then continued heading downstream to where Mom was preparing their picnic lunch.

A few minutes later, Mom saw them coming, left the opened jar of peanut butter and jelly, the loaf of bread, and the cookies on their picnic blanket, and came down to the stream with a towel for the kids. Dad had already found a comfortable place to relax, leaning up against a tree, when suddenly Noah yelled, *"Bear!"*

Then Jonah began shouting, *"Bear!"* and pointing in the direction of the tree where Dad was sitting.

Mom looked where they were pointing and thought, *It's just a shaggy German Shepherd dog.* She had seen a couple big dogs just a few moments before with their owners who were hiking the trail above them.

That's when Hannah started screaming, *"Bear!"*

Suddenly, Mom realized that what was standing on the other side of the tree where Dad was sitting was *NOT* a dog. It was a bear! "Dad!" she yelled hysterically, "Look behind your tree. It *is* a bear!"

Dad took one look and shouted to the kids, "Don't run!" because he knew bears would lose interest in people if they didn't have any food, if they looked big, and if they didn't run. But, if you run, bears have been known to enjoy a good chase.

It was too late, as Mom and the three kids were already gone, running as fast as their legs would carry them across the stream and toward the car.

Dad stood up slowly and raised his hands above his head to look as big as possible and started backing away from the big, shaggy brownish-black bear.

The bear began to follow him. Dad's heart was beating wildly. Then the bear turned slowly and walked over to the picnic blanket that Mom had spread out, and stuck his nose in the jar of peanut butter with the stripes of jelly, grabbed the loaf of bread, and lumbered off in the direction of two more bears that could now be seen on the hillside.

By this time, Dad realized that he was not in any immediate danger, so he took out his cell phone camera and took a few pictures. Then he watched the bear until it disappeared into the woods.

All this time the kids thought the reason Dad wasn't coming was because he had gotten killed by the bear. How relieved they were, especially Noah, when Dad walked into the clearing and calmly climbed into the car.

A few minutes later, a forest ranger appeared. He had been alerted to the sighting of the bears and came to make sure everyone was safe. "We're safe," Mom commented, "but we don't feel real comfortable about getting out of the car and picking up what's left of our picnic."

The ranger nodded and said he'd be happy to pick up their stuff for them.

Photo taken by: Chrystique Neibauer

For the next few days, all the kids could talk about was the bear that ate their picnic lunch. Finally Noah admitted, "You know, thinking about a bear is scarier than actually seeing one, especially when you know Jesus can protect you." ∎

> *The LORD will keep you from all harm—*
> *he will watch over your life;*
> *the LORD will watch over your coming and going*
> *both now and forevermore.*
> *—Psalm 121:7, 8, NIV*

Cheap Shampoo

Melissa ran a brush through her long, dark blonde hair and tied it back in a quick ponytail. "Bye, Mom, I'm leaving for school!" she called as she raced out the door. Thursdays were her least favorite day of the week. She had math, followed by English, then science, but it was computer studies she was dreading. A group of popular girls were in that class and the way they looked her up and down made her cringe.

Before she knew it, Melissa was walking into the computer lab. She smoothed down her shirt, suddenly aware that it was a hand-me-down from her older sister. Her jeans had been a birthday present from Aunt Michelle last winter and although they were still nice, they were just a fraction too short to look right. She tightened her ponytail and relaxed. *At least I have nice hair.* On good days, they didn't tease her about her clothes, but complimented about her beautiful hair instead. Maybe

today would be one of those days.

Just then, Abigail walked past and gave her a small smile. Abigail was a rather shy girl and Melissa hadn't really gotten to know her even though they were in a couple of classes together. And if anyone was less fashionably dressed than Melissa, it was Abigail. Her clothes looked like they had been handed down three or four times before they made their way to Abigail's wardrobe.

Melissa waited for the teacher to arrive and got out her textbook in anticipation. When she looked up, Melissa felt her stomach sink. The group of girls, in their pretty new tops and pretty new jeans and pretty new shoes, had surrounded Abigail.

"Hey, Abigail," said Felicity, twirling strands of her long, wavy hair around her finger. "Whatcha doin'?"

Abigail squirmed under the sudden attention, but pulled herself up tall in her chair. Her voice was quiet but firm. "Nothing. Just getting ready for class."

Tiffany pulled back Abigail's computer chair and spun it around so she was facing them. She then stood back, crossed her arms, and let her gaze run over Abigail's outfit from top to bottom, then back again. "Girl, you've got your own style going on there, haven't you?"

Melissa cringed as the other girls laughed.

"I've got more important things to think about than clothes," Abigail said, although Melissa heard a wobble in her voice.

Tiffany and her friends started firing questions at her that really weren't questions at all.

"So, which charity shop did you get your shirt from?"

"And your shoes. Where did you get them? They're so worn out,

they probably stink." The girls giggled and waved their hands in front of their noses to get rid of an imaginary bad smell.

Amber grabbed a handful of Abigail's reddish-blonde hair. "And you really should do something about this hair, Abigail."

The group laughed again, and Tiffany reached out to touch Amber's perfectly curled hair. "What sort of shampoo do you use, Amber? Your hair is just to die for."

"I use *Absolute Deluxe* by Jarrod Haine," she said. "You can only get it from the hairdresser and it costs twenty dollars a bottle."

"That's nothing," said Felicity. "You know that shampoo that Ava Thomas, the movie star, uses? My mom bought me some of that last week. It was so expensive."

Inside Melissa, a flame of anger was starting to grow. *What does it matter what kind of shampoo someone uses?* She looked at Abigail who had her head bowed, her shoulders now slumped and sagging.

The group of girls continued to compare expensive hair care products that Melissa had never heard of, let alone used. Her mom said most of the time with expensive brands, you were paying for the name on the label. *Why waste the money if cheap shampoo works just as well?*

"So Abigail," said Amber, "what brand of shampoo do you use?"

Abigail didn't even raise her head. She studied her chipped and broken fingernails in silence. Tiffany bumped her on the shoulder, hard. "Answer the question," she snarled. "What kind of shampoo do you use?" Tiffany pretended to sniff Abigail's hair. She waved her hand in front of her nose. "*Pee-uuuuu!* From the smell of that I'm guessing you use dog shampoo."

The other girls thought it was hilarious. Abigail slumped lower in her seat and suddenly looked very small. Melissa's anger burned red hot in her chest.

It was Felicity's turn. Her words were sweetly spoken but her eyes were steely cold. "Come on, Abigail. We really want to know. You can tell us. What kind of shampoo do you use?"

Abigail answered in a whisper so quiet, Melissa couldn't hear her.

Tiffany thumped Abigail on the shoulder again. "Speak up," she demanded.

Abigail answered again, more loudly this time. "I said *Fashion Fundamentals*."

The group of girls burst out laughing so hard anyone would've thought they'd just heard the funniest joke on the planet.

"Did you hear that?" said Amber. "*Fashion Fundamentals*. That stuff's so bad you find it in the throw-out bin at the dollar store."

The flames grew hotter in Melissa's chest. That was it. Melissa was on her feet before she knew it. She stood squarely in front of the group of nasty girls and held her chin high. Ignoring them, she looked directly at Abigail and smiled. "I use *Fashion Fundamentals* too," she said. Melissa tossed her ponytail, sending her soft, blonde hair back and forth across her shoulders. "And if you ask me, anything else is a waste of money. The ingredients are practically the same as *Absolute Deluxe*, just some people aren't clever enough to realize it."

Abigail looked surprised at first, but her surprise soon turned into a smile as the group of girls around her stood speechless. She sat up straight in her chair and grinned at Melissa.

Melissa lifted her gaze from Abigail to Tiffany, Amber, and Felicity, her eyes strong and confident, daring any one of them to challenge her. They didn't. Instead, like a pack of wolves who knew they were beaten, they mumbled something about having to sit down before the teacher arrived and crept away.

Melissa smiled. She couldn't help but notice the relief on Abigail's face. Joy welled up inside her, knowing she had stood up for what was right.

Melissa hurriedly packed up her things and settled into the seat next to Abigail just as Mr. Walker ambled into the room with an arm full of books. Abigail reached out and gave her hand a squeeze of thanks. Maybe computer studies wasn't going to be so bad after all. ■

> *Before destruction the heart of a man is haughty,*
> *and before honor is humility.*
> —Proverbs 18:12, NKJV

The 10K Race

Jim crawled out from beneath his downy comforter and shivered. *This is insane,* he thought as he slid his feet blindly about the floor in search of his slippers. *I could sleep an extra hour and a half before getting dressed for school if I hadn't talked Dad into running the Father-Son 10K Race with me.*

A few weeks earlier when Jim had seen the brightly colored poster in the supermarket, it had sounded like so much fun. He and his friends had badgered their dads to enter. Not all the dads had agreed, but Jim was pleased that his dad was willing to enter this special event with him. Now, at 4:30 in the morning, it no longer seemed like a great idea. What he hadn't counted on was all the training it was going to take to get into shape to run ten kilometers—which is 6.2 miles.

Jim yawned. Only the sound of water running in the bathroom sink kept Jim from climbing back into bed. "Dad's already up," he groaned. Using all the self-control he could muster, Jim got out of bed, stretched, then peeked through the blinds into the predawn darkness outside his window. A mantle of early morning mist shrouded the streetlights. He quickly shed his pajamas for his sweat suit and running shoes. Five minutes later, he and his father were stretching to prepare for their morning run.

During the first week of training, Jim had stood by the bathroom door each morning at 4:30 urging his dad to hurry. But now, five weeks into their training and with the mornings getting colder, Jim's enthusiasm had dimmed. However, Jim knew that once his father agreed to a plan, he would see it to the end. Dad often quoted Luke 9:62, "No one, having put his hand to the plow, and looking back, is fit for the kingdom of God." *And Dad has definitely put his hand to the plow!* thought Jim as he retied a loose shoelace.

A chilling breeze slapped Jim awake as he stepped onto the front porch. "Come on," Dad called, "let's make tracks." Jim groaned and then fell into place beside his father. After running the first block, the two runners fell into a smooth rhythm. Only the sound of their tennis shoes slapping the pavement and an occasional passing vehicle broke the silence of their early morning world.

By the time they completed their route and finished their cooling down routine, Jim was feeling almost human again.

"Good run, son." Dad patted Jim on the shoulder and headed up the stairs to shower for work. "I think it's time we add another mile."

"Another mile?" Jim rolled his eyes and stumbled into the kitchen for a glass of orange juice. "It will be a miracle if I survive until the race," he mumbled.

Jim asked his dad how he managed to keep going.

"I have a secret weapon," his father admitted.

"A secret weapon?"

"Yep. You'll find it in Isaiah 40:30, 31."

"Awww, Dad," Jim groaned. "I thought you really had something."

"Don't knock it until you try it."

Jim thought of his friends and their dads. While they had all begun training for the race together, most had dropped out after the first few mornings.

Jim opened his Bible and found his father's secret weapon. "Even youths grow tired and weary, and young men stumble and fall; but those who hope in the LORD will renew their strength. They will soar on wings like eagles; they will run and not grow weary, they will walk and not be faint."

Jim straightened his shoulders and smiled to himself. *Hmmm, I think Dad's talking about God being his running partner.*

The morning of the race, Jim slipped the number harness over his

red and white running jersey—207. Dad was runner 208. The two of them bent down to check the laces of their well-worn sneakers, then stood up and adjusted the waistbands on their running shorts and took some deep breaths.

"Ready, son?" Dad asked, waving to Mom and to Jim's two younger brothers standing by her side. Jim waved too. Further down the row of well-wishers were his best friends, Tom and Bill. They exchanged victorious "thumbs-up" with him.

I'm really going through with this, he thought. A surge of excitement caused the little hairs on Jim's neck to tingle. "Yes, I am," he whispered through his clenched teeth.

The starting gun sounded and the runners surged forward from behind the line. Within a short distance, the runners had strung out over the course, each team falling into their natural stride. A few teams of runners broke free of the pack. This disturbed Jim. He didn't like having other teams ahead of him. He was tempted to step up their pace. But Dad had cautioned that this would happen—that some of the less-experienced runners would sprint ahead and use up all their energy too early in the race, leaving nothing for the last hill. "The object is to finish the race, son," Dad reminded.

At the beginning of the race, the morning sun felt good on Jim's back as he covered the first few kilometers of the course. But as time passed, it intensified. Sweat poured down his back and chest and dripped off the end of his nose. Jim gulped a cup of water at each watering hole and ran on. Every so often, he heard his friends or his family cheering him on. When their shouts faded, he knew they'd hopped in the car and would drive to the next point.

Way station after way station passed. Jim and his dad ran side by side. It felt good to know his dad was there, matching him, pacing him, running with him every step of the way.

As they climbed Blossom Hill, Jim remembered his dad's warning about picking up too much speed on the way down the other side. Suddenly, a small boy in the crowd broke free of his mother and darted in front of Jim. Jim swerved to avoid the child, lost his balance, and stumbled to one knee. Out of the corner of his eye, Jim watched other teams charge on by. Blood streamed from his scraped knee and hand.

Angry tears sprang into his eyes.

"Are you hurt bad, son?" Dad bent down to look at Jim's injury.

"Naw, I don't think so. It looks worse than it is."

Someone from the audience thrust a clean, cotton handkerchief into

Jim's hand. He tied it around his injured knee and stood up.

"Ready to go on?" his father asked.

"Now? After this?"

"I am if you are."

Jim nodded. "Sure, why not."

The finish line came into view. The first team had broken the ribbon. Five more teams crossed the line before Jim and his dad. Once across the line, Jim's family and friends engulfed them. Tom thrust a bottle of water into Jim's hand while Bill dumped a second one over Jim's head. Jim eyed his bottle and then his dad. Before his dad could see it coming, he poured it all over his father's head.

Dad laughed and grabbed his son and gave him a giant bear hug. They had completed the race together, and that alone made them winners. It had been a difficult race. Having family and friends cheer him on had been great. But the best part, Jim decided, was that his father was not on the sidelines cheering him on, but beside him every step of the way.

He smiled to himself as he thought about how God is like that. *Dear heavenly Father,* he prayed, *I'm so glad You have promised to always run by my side every step of the way, and that I'm never really alone. Thank You, God, for being such an awesome running Partner!* ∎

I will be with you; I will never leave you nor forsake you.
—Joshua 1:5, NIV

Lawnmower Caper

Mark jumped out of the apple tree and landed on the grass next to his younger sister, Kimmie. "Whatcha doin'?"

"Looking at that giant sailing ship!" Kimmie was lying on her back in the grass, her arms folded beneath her head, and staring up at the white, puffy clouds. "See, over there." She pointed toward the sky above the silo on Grandpa's red barn.

"Yeah!" Mark stared up at the clouds floating by. "There's a humpback whale." He pointed to his left.

Kimmie clicked her tongue. "No, that's an elephant. He has a trunk and big ears."

"Aww, you're seeing things." Determined to identify another shape in the clouds, Mark squinted. "That could almost be a bullet train."

Kimmie nodded thoughtfully. "Or a dead boa constrictor."

"Dead?"

"Well, it's all stretched out like a

dead snake," she reasoned.

"That's why it looks like a big ole bullet train."

"*Hmmph!* I think I'd recognize a bullet train if I saw one!" Kimmie jumped to her feet. "I'm bored!"

"Me too!" Mark placed his hands on his hips. "We could jump in the hay again."

"No. We already did that. And we climbed the apple trees and made hay tunnels and petted the kittens and fed the chickens . . ."

Every summer, Mark and Kimmie spent a week at their grandma and grandpa's farm in southern Texas. Now their visit was almost over and they had run out of new and exciting things to do.

"Too bad Grandma is still at the store or we could help her make sugar cookies."

"Yeah." Mark's stomach growled.

Grandma managed a fabric store in town, about a mile from the farm. Soon after Grandma left for work, Grandpa had to make an emergency run to the tractor store to replace a broken part. He'd asked the children if they wanted to go with him, but they decided that they didn't want to spend the day riding to the next county in Grandpa's old, rusty pickup truck with no air-conditioning.

After reminding the kids of some important safety rules about being home alone, Grandpa climbed into his truck. "I'll be back as soon as possible," he called as he drove out of the yard.

As the sun rose higher in the sky, Mark and Kimmie grew hungry. It was an hour or so before lunchtime, but they had eaten breakfast early. They tromped into Grandma's pantry looking for something that didn't need to be warmed up on the stove, which was one of the safety rules on Grandpa's list.

"There's always peanut butter and jelly sandwiches," Kimmie volunteered.

"I guess." Mark sighed. "Are all the cookies gone?"

Kimmie peered into Grandma's giant gingerbread house cookie jar. "Yep, every crumb."

Mark walked over to the refrigerator and poured himself a glass of ice-cold milk. "I'm gonna watch some TV. Grandpa didn't say anything about not watching television."

"Good idea." Kimmie poured herself a small glass of milk and followed her brother to the family room. Mark picked up the remote and began flipping through the channels—news, soap operas, talk shows, and game shows. "Ah, here's something about sharks," he announced and kicked back into Grandpa's leather recliner. Kimmie made herself comfortable in her favorite chair. During the first commercial break there was an ad for "toaster pastries."

"*Mmm,* that looks *sooo* good." Kimmie licked her lips. "I wish I had one of those right now!" Suddenly, a peanut butter and jelly sandwich didn't appeal to her.

"Me too. Wow! Maybe Grandma has a box of toaster pastries in the pantry." He hopped out of the recliner and bounded to the kitchen pantry. Electrified at the idea, Kimmie charged after her brother. They found pancake flour, sugar, cold cereal, even English muffins, but no toaster pastries.

"Oh," Mark groaned and rubbed his stomach. "I want a toaster pastry so badly."

"Me too," Kimmie whined. "One filled with strawberry."

"No, I want a blueberry one."

"*Hmmm,* blueberry sounds good too." Kimmie sighed. "We could walk to Mrs. Collins' Country Grocery and buy some. Grandma has an account there."

"Yeah, but it's a mile away and it's too hot to walk anywhere today." Mark frowned and pursed his lips. He could almost taste that blueberry pastry as he headed back to the family room.

On his way, Mark glanced out the window. Setting in the shade of the garage was Grandpa's self-propelled, hand-guided lawnmower. Mark whirled about to face his sister. "What if we rode Grandpa's lawnmower into town? Grandpa never said anything about not riding his lawnmower!"

"You've got to be kidding. How would we do that?"

"Don't worry. I've got it all figured out. It might be weird, but it sure beats walking." Mark dashed out of the house. He and Kimmie hauled the lawnmower out of the yard and onto the blacktop road. Mark pulled the starter cord, tied a rope around the handle to keep the motor from stopping, and aimed the machine down the center of the road toward town. "It's moving! It's moving! It's going to work!"

Mark jumped on top of the mower. "Come on! Jump on! You can do it."

Uncertain, Kimmie ran beside the mower for a few feet. Just as she leaped onto the machine beside her brother, a monster-sized oil truck crested the hill coming straight for them. With no time to leap off the lawnmower into the ditch, the children closed their eyes, certain they were about to be squashed like june bugs on the screen door. But no, the driver honked his air horn, swung his truck into the other lane, and passed.

"Maybe we'd better move to the side of the road," Mark suggested.

"You think so?" Kimmie said sarcastically. She was terrified! But before they could aim the slow-moving mower to the side of the road, a flashy, white Cadillac sped by, barely missing them.

With no one guiding the lawnmower by the handle, it wandered to the right and to the left. Every few minutes, Mark or Kimmie would have to jump off the mower to straighten it. It took a while, but they finally reached the little country store on the edge of town. Both of the kids sighed with relief when they stepped inside and felt the cool air. Mrs. Collins, the store owner, recognized them immediately.

"Kimmie and Mark, what a pleasant surprise. It's mighty hot out there today. Your faces are sunburned. Did you walk to town?"

"Sort of," Mark mumbled. He sensed that Mrs. Collins might not approve of their means of transportation.

Mrs. Collins nodded and smiled. "May I help you with something?"

Mark stepped up to the counter. "We'd like two boxes of toaster pastries, one strawberry and one blueberry, please."

"They're right over there, beside the boxed cereals." She pointed to her left. "It's been a long time since anyone has asked for toaster pastries."

Mark found the desired pastry boxes and placed them on the counter beside the cash register. "Please charge this to my grandmother's account."

"I'll do that." Mrs. Collins opened her green ledger book and recorded the charge. "Enjoy your pastries, kids."

"Oh, we will," Kimmie assured Mrs. Collins, then followed Mark out of the store.

"Let's eat one now." Mark started to open the package of blueberry pastries.

"No, wait. They'll taste lots better if we can heat them in the toaster and have cold milk to drink with them."

Within a short time, the two children started the lawnmower and headed home. They had gotten the hang of jumping off the lawnmower to straighten it out and then jumping back on again.

They hadn't gone far, however, when a familiar pickup truck rolled up beside them and stopped. It was Mr. Bigelow, who lived next door to their grandparents. He leaped from his truck, looking much bigger than his usual six-foot, four-inch height and his two-hundred pound weight.

"What are you kids doing?" he called.

Frightened, Kimmie hid behind her brother as Mark stumbled over his words trying to explain why they were riding Grandpa's lawnmower. Mr. Bigelow scowled and shook his head. "Get into the truck while I load the lawnmower into the back. I'll take you to your grandparents' place."

"Yes, sir," the children mumbled as they climbed into the front seat. A few minutes later, Mr. Bigelow deposited Mark and Kimmie and the lawnmower at the farm. He left them with a warning to never, ever pull such a stunt again. Relieved that Grandpa wasn't home yet, they hastily agreed.

After Mr. Bigelow's truck was no longer in sight, the children rushed inside the house and ran straight to the kitchen. Kimmie could almost taste the thick, strawberry jelly oozing out of the pressed-together pastries and into her mouth. She went to drop her pastry into the toaster slot when she screeched, *"Eewh!"*

"What's the matter with you?" Mark said as he quickly ripped the top off his box.

"Bugs!" She flung the pastry box to the other side of the pantry. "Weevils! The box is full of weevils!"

"Too bad. If you're nice to me, I'll share my—*eewh!*" He dropped his blueberry pastry onto the floor. Little brown bugs scurried out of his box and onto his hands. "Yuck! Who wants to eat weevils in their toaster pastries? Not me!"

"Me neither!" Kimmie exclaimed as she quickly brushed the live critters from her hands and arms. "It's not fair! We worked so hard to get our pastries only to have them filled with weevils!"

"Who would have guessed that the boxes on Mrs. Collins' shelves would be old and full of weevils?"

That night at worship, Grandpa thanked God for protecting Kimmie and Mark.

"You were very blessed today," Grandma reminded them. "You could have lost your lives out on that road. I'm sure you have learned a very important lesson."

"Yeah, not to ride a lawnmower into town for toaster pastries." Mark rolled his eyes toward the ceiling.

Grandma nodded wisely. "That's one lesson, but another is the things you see on television aren't always as good as you imagine them to be. The toaster pastries weren't worth risking your lives for, were they?"

"That's right," Grandpa added. "There are other things, too, that you think you gotta have, but in the end, aren't so great."

Mark's eyes grew serious. "Yeah, like taking drugs or drinking beer! It may look like fun, but in the end, it's bad for you."

"And smoking cigarettes!" Kimmie added.

"That's right, honey." Grandpa patted his granddaughter's head. "If you ask God to help you make good decisions, He will." ■

I will give you a wise and discerning heart.
— 1 Kings 3:12, NIV

Lori's Love Cup

Lately, Lori was acting downright obnoxious! Before breakfast, she shouted at her sister, "That's mine. I had it first!" as she grabbed a doll away from little sister, Lisa. A little later, Lori teased, "You're just a scaredy-cat," when Lisa was afraid to go down the slide.

After supper, Lisa wanted to listen to the CD that Lori was playing. "Get out of my room!" yelled Lori. "It's private and you don't belong. Get out! O-U-T spells out!" And Lori slammed the door.

By bedtime, Mom was exhausted just from hearing her all day. "Lori, your words have been so sour today, I feel like giving you a lemon to suck on." Mom turned and shook her head.

Lori went to sleep that night in a foul mood. And she woke up the same way. Mom was just about ready to give Lori what she richly deserved, when she got an idea.

"Lori," she said, "I think I know what's wrong with you!"

"What's wrong with me?" Lori said,

quite annoyed that her mom would imply something was wrong with her.

"Lori, I think your love cup is empty!"

"My what?" asked Lori.

"Your love cup," said Mom. "I think it's empty. What you need is to get filled to overflowing with love so you have enough love to give away. Come over here, Lori, and let me fill you up."

Lori wasn't sure she should get too close to Mom. She knew what she deserved!

But Mom smiled, wrapped her in her arms, and said, "I love you."

"Is your love cup filled up yet?" Mom asked.

"Well," answered Lori, "it's up to here," pointing to her waist.

So Mom hugged and kissed Lori once more and again whispered, "I love you" in Lori's ear.

"Is your love cup filled now?" Mom asked.

"Well, it's up to here," Lori said with a gleam in her eyes as she pointed to her chin.

Once again, Mom hugged Lori, then looked her in the eyes and said, "Lori, you'll always be my special girl. And I love you this much," she said as she stretched out her arms as far as possible.

"Now," asked Mom, "is your love cup full?"

"Yes," Lori replied, her eyes glistening with happiness. "It's so full, it's overflowing."

"Oh, good," said Mom. "Now you have enough love to give away. Why don't you start by giving your sister a little hug?"

"Oh no," said Lori, "Lisa will just push me away."

"Well," said Mom, "that's probably what you deserve after the way you've been treating her. But you have so much love now it's spilling over the top. It wouldn't hurt to waste a little on your sister, would it?"

Lori shook her head and ran to find Lisa. "I love you!" she said as she flung her arms around her little sister, giving her a great big bear hug. And much to Lori's surprise, Lisa hugged her right back!

But that's not the end of the story . . .

A couple weeks later Mom was having a terrible day.

At breakfast, she burned the toast. After lunch, the sink got plugged up and water ran all over the kitchen floor.

Then, just as she was about to leave to pick up the girls from school, she discovered she had locked the keys inside the car! By the time she picked up Lori and Lisa, Mom was in a really bad mood. "Hurry and get in the car!" Mom yelled. "Can't you see I'm late?"

The girls got in the car, buckled their seat belts and began to giggle.

"Girls," complained Mom, "stop the giggling. I've got a headache and can't stand the noise!"

And when they got home, Mom's mood didn't seem to improve. Mom was being obnoxious!

"I think I know what's wrong with you," Lori said to her mom.

"What's wrong with me?" growled Mom.

"Yes, I mean . . . well, I think your love cup is empty," said Lori as she ran up and gave her Mom a great big hug. "I think so too," chimed in Lisa, making it a group hug.

A big smile crossed Mom's face.

"Now, is your love cup filled?" asked Lori.

"Not quite," Mom said with a twinkle in her eye.

Lisa and Lori quickly planted kisses on each of Mom's cheeks.

"Is your love cup filled now?" they asked, excitedly waiting for her answer.

"Yes, girls. Yes, it is. My love cup is full and overflowing!" ■

> *Love is patient, love is kind. . . . It is not rude.*
> —1 Corinthians 13:4, 5, NIV

Worry-Wart

C reeeak! Creeeak!

Philip wrapped his pillow even tighter around his head. *What was that?* he thought. He tried to listen and get deeper under his covers at the same time. He could just barely hear his dad's voice. "Did you guys have fun, Alice?"

The pillow fell away from Philip's ears. It was just his sister, Alice, coming in through the front door. He laid there in his almost dark room with his eyes wide open. He always stayed awake for a long time after he went to bed. He had a lot to worry about—and sometimes he was afraid of the dark.

Philip's mom was sick. Tonight, she was in the hospital again, and Philip wasn't sure when she was coming home. His dad cooked and made sure he had what he needed. His sister dropped him off at school and picked him up at the end of the day.

But no one tucked him in at night

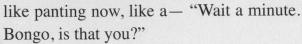

like his mother did. And his room seemed scarier at night.

Creeeak! Philip could see his door slowly moving open. He grabbed his pillow and ducked under the covers. Then he felt something bump his bed. *What's out there?* he worried. From under the covers he heard a heavy breathing sound. It got louder. He listened closer. It sounded

like panting now, like a— "Wait a minute. Bongo, is that you?"

The answer was a happy whine. Philip pushed the covers away and reached over to pet his dog, Bongo, on the head. "You scared me, Bongo. Aren't you supposed to be outside by now?" Bongo always slept outside in his house, but it was nice to see him inside this time.

Philip scratched Bongo behind his ear the way he liked. "I bet you don't have any problem going to sleep," he said. Bongo licked Philip's hand. "You probably don't even worry about Mom." Bongo whined a little to say that he did worry. "OK, I know you miss her too. I just wish she would get well and come home."

He was still talking to Bongo when his door *creeeaked* again. This time, his dad's head poked around the door. "Bongo," Dad said quietly, "so this is where you are. I've been looking all over for you. You're supposed to be outside, not in here keeping Philip awake."

"It's OK, Dad. Bongo is keeping me company." Philip leaned back onto his pillow as his dad sat down on the side of the bed and took over scratching Bongo's head. "Dad, when is Mom coming home?"

Dad patted Philip's leg. "You remember what the doctor said. If this treatment goes well, she'll be home in two days. Or it might be three or four days. But she'll be home soon." He looked at Philip and smiled sadly, "You're worried about her, aren't you?"

Philip nodded. "It's hard to go to sleep. And then I hear things in the dark and I'm not sure what they are." He rolled over and stared at the wall. "I just wish Mom was home."

"I wish she was too, son," Dad said. "And she will be, as soon as she can."

"Dad, do you worry too?" Philip asked in a very quiet voice.

"Yes, I do."

Then he was quiet for so long that Philip asked another question. "What do you do when you're too worried to do anything—even to go to sleep?"

"I do a lot of things," Dad answered. "I go to the hospital to visit your mom. I stay busy at work and taking care of you and Alice." He reached over and ruffed up the fur on Bongo's head. "I even take Bongo out for a long walk. But the most important thing I do is this—I talk to God."

"You mean you pray?" Philip asked.

"Yes," Dad said, "but I don't always stop and kneel or even close my eyes. Sometimes I just talk to God out loud and tell Him that I'm worried about your mom or that I'm not sure I'm doing the right things for you or your sister."

Philip sat up. "You just talk to God? Like I talk to you? Or to Bongo?"

Dad laughed. "Well, yes. Just like you're talking to your best friend. God loves us. He wants us to be happy and healthy. But sometimes things happen that we don't like."

Photo taken by: Chelsea Bond

"Like Mom getting sick?"

"That's right. Sometimes people get sick or get hurt. God doesn't keep those things from happening, but He does help us. He is helping the doctors who are treating your mom, and He's helping me handle everything while she's away. One of the best things about being a Christian is that we don't have to worry about things we can't control, things like Mom being

Photo taken by: Chelsea Bond

sick. We can hand the problems over to Jesus and trust Him to take care of them." Then Dad got up and stood beside the bed. "OK, Bongo, let's go. You have a warm doghouse waiting for you. Good night, Philip."

Philip listened to the quiet house for a few minutes after his dad left. Then he looked up at the ceiling and said, "Dear God, I'm worried about Mom. I want her to get well and come home. But help me not to be too worried. I know You're taking care of her—and of me. I love You, Jesus. Good night." Then he closed his eyes.

Scrape! Clang! Clink! The noise woke Philip up fast. He grabbed at his pillow, then noticed something. "Hey, it's morning already!" he said out loud. "I went right to sleep after talking to God!" As he pushed back the covers, he could hear his dad fixing breakfast and talking to Bongo in the kitchen. "Settle down, you silly dog. I'm getting your breakfast too."

Photo taken by: Chelsea Bond

Philip smiled and hopped out of bed. "I'm not going to be a worry-wart anymore!" ∎

Therefore I say to you, do not worry about your life, what you will eat or what you will drink; nor about your body, what you will put on. Is not life more than food and the body more than clothing?
—Matthew 6:25, NKJV